D1267946

STUDIES IN THE ECONOMIC DEVELOPMENT
OF INDIA
Edited by Professor P. N. Rosenstein-Rodan

5

INVESTMENTS FOR CAPACITY EXPANSION

STUDIES IN THE ECONOMIC DEVELOPMENT OF INDIA

INVESTMENTS FOR CAPACITY EXPANSION
Size, Location, and Time-Phasing

EDITED BY

[ALAN S. MANNE]

Professor of Economics
Stanford University

THE M.I.T. PRESS
MASSACHUSETTS INSTITUTE OF TECHNOLOGY
Cambridge, Massachusetts

For

PITAMBAR PANT

Perspective Planner

PREFACE

In times past, impecunious authors employed their prefaces to acknowledge the patronage of a wealthy, enlightened prince. In this more democratic and affluent age, it is the Ford Foundation that is to be thanked. The book was begun in New Delhi at the Center for International Studies, Massachusetts Institute of Technology, and was completed at the Graduate School of Business, Stanford University. Both the beginning and the completion were made possible by Ford Foundation grants to these institutions. The conclusions, opinions and other statements, however, are the sole responsibility of the author.

Because of the hazards of singling out individual friends, it seems preferable to acknowledge help at the appropriate points throughout the text. This procedure—though admirable in principle—would not do justice to the men who first introduced me to India: Max Millikan and Paul Rosenstein-Rodan.

One last set of individual acknowledgements: Both A. N. Natarajan and Eleanor Hingston are to be thanked for the patience and care with which they typed this manuscript. Jacqueline M. is to be thanked for the patience and love with which she treats the author.

Stanford, California
March 1966   ALAN S. MANNE

CONTENTS

PART II. SINGLE PRODUCING AREA— FURTHER RESULTS

PART III. MULTIPLE PRODUCING AREAS— FURTHER RESULTS

LIST OF FIGURES

PART I

FOUR INDUSTRY STUDIES

CHAPTER 1

INTRODUCTION

ALAN S. MANNE

This volume is concerned with planning investments in a series of future manufacturing facilities. Case studies are reported for four heavy process industries in India: aluminium, caustic soda, cement, and nitrogenous fertilizers. In these sectors, there are significant economies-of-scale in manufacturing, and there is a close interdependence between the size, location and time-phasing of new capacity.

Problems of investment planning have both a theoretical and a practical side. They are of common interest to managers, engineers, operations researchers, and economists. In preliminary presentations of this material, the author has observed that the type of question raised depends heavily upon the individual's professional background. The manager or engineer is usually concerned with the practical relevance, the realism and the transferability of these studies; the operations researcher tends to concentrate on the algorithmic and the uncertainty aspects; and the economist focuses upon the implications for development planning. Accordingly, it appears desirable to begin with a few paragraphs addressed to each separate group of readers.

Relevance, realism, and transferability

The analyses described here were intended for application within the Indian economy as it was operating during the mid-1960s. Some features relate to the specific conditions of India, and would have limited transferability across national boundaries. Within the USA, to take an extreme contrast, the size and location of a new cement plant would be determined by a cold techno-economic calculation of private costs and benefits.[1] In India, a similar decision would be subject to the push-and-pull of regional and local interests operating through a parliamentary democracy. Accordingly, our models emphasize a feature which would be far less significant in the US cement industry than in India—an explicit calculation of the economic costs of satisfying demands raised through political channels

---

[1] It would be a mistake to suppose that all investment decisions within the USA are based upon cold calculations. Martin Shubik has commented that the size and location of an industrial research laboratory are likely to be heavily influenced by the monument building propensities of an elderly vice president.

by regional and local pressure groups. Nevertheless, to the extent that both the Indian and the US manager are responsible for economizing upon the resource inputs needed in order to achieve specified outputs, there is a similarity in their outlook on the problems of investment choice—and perhaps some international transferability in the mathematical models.[1]

The viewpoint here is that of a preliminary investment survey, one that provides a rough framework within which to draw up a detailed proposal on the *next* project to be built. The conclusions of such a preinvestment survey are intended to serve as the initial premises for a specific project: when, where, and how large a unit to construct.

It is not within the scope of this volume to deal with the evaluation of specific projects. Instead, the reader is referred to a standard survey on project evaluation, United Nations, Economic Commission for Latin America (1958). For practical ideas on how to find the best site for *one* new plant—and for a private enterprise orientation—see Bierwert and Krone (1955).

In a preliminary survey, a more aggregate viewpoint is appropriate than in the evaluation of a specific project. Details on the process, the site, the product-mix, etc., can be handled by broad-brush assumptions in the one stage of analysis but not in the other. Example: In the Indian nitrogenous fertilizer industry (Chapter 7 below), we assumed that a fertilizer complex would produce a 'typical' product-mix of ammonium sulphate and urea—and did not pursue the implications of alternate product-mixes. However, in evaluating a specific fertilizer project (with its specific size, location, and date) it then becomes appropriate to consider alternate product-mixes rather than just a single one. This difference in level of detail depends upon a conjecture and a judgment—that the general conclusions on size, location and time-phasing would not be upset by plausible variations in the product-mix.

The product-mix example is typical of what happens in formulating a mathematical model, or indeed in setting up any other logical calculating procedure. Simplifications are inevitable. Mathematical decision models are not intended to be fully realistic. They are intended only to be realistic enough so as to be useful in arriving at sound decisions. It is always the analyst's responsibility to exercise

[1] It was only after these studies were completed that the author became aware of the work proceeding simultaneously in the Soviet Union upon this class of investment problems. Ward (1965) summarizes the plant size, location and time-phasing studies of Birman (ceramic pipe) and Loginov and Minc (cement). In the USA, similar work has been reported by Buzby (Union Carbide) and by Welter (Coastal States Gas Producing Company) at the 28th National Meeting of the Operations Research Societ of America, Houston, Texas, November 1965.

sufficient care, judgment and imagination so that the principal conclusions remain insensitive to his simplifications.

Algorithms and computations

To a mathematician, the principal feature of these investment programming problems is that they entail the minimization of a non-convex function subject to linear inequality constraints. Because of economies-of-scale in the manufacturing costs, a local optimum is not a global one. The challenge consists of finding optimal solutions in special cases—and in devising satisfactory approximations for more general cases where a rigorously optimal solution is computationally infeasible. On these non-convex problems, Bellman and Dreyfus (1962, p. 83) observe:

'The problem of distinguishing an absolute maximum from relative maxima is one that plagues the optimization field. It cannot be expected that it will ever be overcome at one blow. What we can hope to accomplish is to add class after class of problems to our zoo of tame specimens.'

It turns out that there are effective methods for optimizing the size of successive plants located within a single producing area, with demands increasing over time. The single area problem is closely related to a well-known class of models: warehousing capacity, equipment replacement and overhaul; checkout, repair, and replacement of stochastically failing equipment; determination of economic lot size, product assortment, and deterministic batch queueing policies; labour force planning; and multi-commodity warehouse decisions. On the mathematical equivalence of all these applications, see Veinott and Wagner (1962). In one variant or another, these models may all be solved through the recursive optimality technique of dynamic programming.

In principle, the multiple producing area model of plant size, location, and time-phasing—like that for the single area—can be solved through a recursive optimality technique. The obstacle is the cost of computations. There are far too many state variables—one for each producing area—hence as many as 15 state variables in the Indian problems considered below. Even with the most powerful available present-day equipment, it would be prohibitively expensive to apply a brute force dynamic programming approach to these cases.[1] It is for this reason that we have turned to a variety of

---

[1] Bellman and Dreyfus (1962, pp. 322–23) suggest that the current state-of-the-art might permit up to three state variables within a dynamic programming calculation.

approximation techniques, rather than concentrating upon exact optimization. Each of these approximations is based upon the restriction of *constant cycle time*, a constant interval of time between the construction of successive plants within a given producing area. This form of policy is known to be optimal for the case of a single producing area that serves a market in which the demand is growing at a constant arithmetic rate over time, and in which the cost functions remain stationary. For the two-area case, numerical experiments are presented in order to check for closeness between the approximation and the solution obtained via dynamic programming.

Most of our effort has gone into obtaining feasible approximate solutions, and comparing them with those that are actually being implemented within the Indian economy.[1] In three of the four cases—the single exception being nitrogenous fertilizers—it turned out that there was a significant cost difference between the existing policies and those suggested by our model. Chapter 8 below contains some speculations on the political and economic reasons for these discrepancies.

Throughout, we have attempted to steer a middle course between the twin pitfalls of over-simplification and of mathematical intractability. It was felt that the studies could not be useful within the Indian economy if the only model considered was the mathematically tractable case, that of a single producing area. A policy-maker is certain to insist upon considering multiple producing areas—even though the mathematician is unable to demonstrate exact optimality for that case. Until the 'curse of dimensionality' is removed from dynamic programming, the multiple area case will have to be solved with an approximation rather than a rigorously exact optimization. To most policy-makers, the mathematical shortcuts are likely to appear far less serious than those taken in producing the basic input data.[2]

Decisions under uncertainty

There is considerable uncertainty associated with each assumption that has entered into these studies. Nevertheless, the calculations

---

[1] Also, lower bounds are constructed on the minimum attainable level of costs. The tightness of these bounds depends upon the particular numerical model.

[2] The numerical precision of our models may be misleading. Upon seeing that we had measured time in hundredths of a year, one keen observer of the Indian scene suggested that the computations ought really to have been carried out to the nearest thousandth. With this more precise time-phasing, a minister could then make a long range forecast whether his inaugural speech for a new plant was to be delivered in the morning or the afternoon.

have been carried out *as though* the future were known with certainty. A single value rather than a probability distribution has been attached to each parameter. The sequential character of investment decisions is ignored. However, when we say that a preinvestment survey is intended only as a framework within which to draw up a detailed proposal on the *next* project to be built, we are really sneaking in one of the precepts of sequential decision-making, 'You can cross that bridge when you come to it'. See Savage (1954, p. 16).

The only form of allowance made here for uncertainty is to follow a time-honoured tradition for deterministic models—sensitivity analysis to check the effects of changing one or more parameters. Nevertheless, the sequential uncertainty problem cannot be conjured away by casual remarks on the possibility of sensitivity analysis. Except in very special formulations of decision models (e.g. the quadratic criterion case of Holt, Modigliani, Muth and Simon (1960)), it is completely illegitimate to replace a probability distribution with a single value for a parameter. More fundamental mathematical work needs to be done in this area.

One special case has already been analysed, and is reported in Manne (1961). This concerns a single producing and consuming area in which the demand is expanding probabilistically over time through a Bachelier-Wiener diffusion process. When installed capacity must always be equal to or greater than demand, it can then be shown unambiguously that the greater the variance of growth in demand, the larger becomes the optimal plant size. For the numerical parameter values analysed, the effect upon the optimal plant size is not of much practical significance unless the variance of the annual increment in demand greatly exceeds the mean value of this increment.

Planning for economic development

For India, unlike a private US enterprise, these sectoral studies are embedded within an economy-wide planning process. In principle, one can think of solving all the elements of an economy-wide programming problem within a single colossal computation—including simultaneously the details of space, time, technological choice, and interindustry relations. In practice, these interlocking details are not solved simultaneously but rather iteratively. Decentralized private and public enterprises respond to the market incentives of cost and profitability—as well as to direct planning.

For the industrial sector of the economy,[1] the iterative mechanism may be sketched with desperate brevity as follows: Every five years,

[1] For an exposition of the political and ideological as well as the economic aspects of the planning process, see Planning Commission (1963).

the Government of India issues a Plan document specifying broad goals in terms of national income and its distribution. The detailed operations of the economy are indicated in terms of a five-year growth target for each major product.[1] These targets are drawn up by individual working groups from the ministries, enterprises, and the Planning Commission. There are official channels for liaison between working groups, but a significant volume of communication also takes place through informal means, e.g. newspaper reports inspired by those managers who are eager to bypass the red tape of official channels. The current operation of the economy is continually monitored through production and consumption statistics. As time passes and as new information becomes available, the Plan targets are revised to become 'likely achievements', taking account of the probable shortfalls and surpluses.

Investment decisions for individual projects are closely related to the sectoral capacity targets established by the five-year Plan document. In response to both the profit motive and to political pressures for regional development, a continuous stream of project proposals flows to New Delhi. There, these proposals are reviewed, papers are shuffled back and forth between many desks, and finally— if the project is approved—an industrial investment licence is issued.

Along with this formal administrative mechanism for planning and control, there are market forces in operation—some of them being illegal. E.g. to cope with the cement shortage prevailing during the mid-1960s, the Government took a pragmatic variety of measures: rationing the non-essential consumers of cement, threatening middlemen who charged prices above the legal ceilings, exhorting the producers to make more efficient use of existing facilities, constructing new cement capacity within the public sector, and creating incentives for private investment through tax reductions and through increased official prices. Similar forces, both market and nonmarket, were at work in each of the four industries studied here. Typically, there were excesses of demand over supply at the official

---

[1] In Perspective Planning Division (1964), detailed physical material balances are published for each of 35 major commodities: coal, petroleum products, electricity, iron ore, manganese ore, limestone, china clay, gypsum, bauxite, chromite, salt, asbestos, cement, sulphuric acid, caustic soda, soda ash, chlorine, calcium carbide, industrial gases, sulphur, phosphorus, rubber, benzene, naphthalene, methanol, phthalic anhydride, formaldehyde, carbon-black, chemical pulp, steel, aluminium, copper, lead, machinery, refractories. These physical balances are intended to check for internal consistency between the output targets generated by each sector's specialized working group. Experiments are also in progress with interindustry models for this purpose. See Chakravarty and Lefeber (1965), Srinivasan (1965), and Manne and Rudra (1965).

prices. The overall shortage of foreign exchange meant that domestic producers were insulated from foreign competition via imports.

Against this untidy background, it is convenient to *idealize* each sector's preinvestment planning process as follows: The Planning Commission tells each working group what will be the demand for that sector's product at each future point in space and time. The Planning Commission also informs each working group as to the future prices for various inputs—both on capital and on current account. On the basis of its specialized sectoral knowledge, the working group chooses a minimum-cost set of plant sizes, locations, etc. Information on the required inputs is then transmitted back to the Planning Commission. We shall not be concerned with how the central authorities determine the demand targets and the input prices, nor how it revises them upon the receipt of new information.[1] We shall simply adopt the partial equilibrium viewpoint of a sectoral working group—that its job is to satisfy the stipulated demands, and to do this at minimum cost, given the appropriate 'shadow' prices for its inputs. In the terminology of neoclassical economics, each sector is viewed as a regulated monopolist in the market for its outputs and as a perfect competitor for its inputs.

Our calculations are built upon a prescriptive view of sectoral planning: single-person cost minimization rather than a multi-person game between the central authorities and the individual enterprises. In Chapter 8 below, it will be suggested that the multi-person viewpoint helps to account for the principal empirical result of these studies—a tendency for India to construct plants that are of less than optimal size.

A preview

For the convenience of readers with diverse interests, this volume is organized into three parts. Part I is addressed to managers, engineers, and economists. It is concerned with the substantive aspects of the four industry studies—the simplifying assumptions made to estimate demands and costs, and the conclusions with respect to size, location and time-phasing. This part is reproduced here essentially as it was written in India during 1963–64. Virtually

[1] Malinvaud (1963) has investigated one such iterative scheme built around decentralized cost minimization—for the case of an economy obeying the postulates of Samuelson's substitution theorem. There is, however, a decisive difference between Malinvaud's problem and this one. Our production sets are non-convex. The optimal plant size problem virtually disappears if convexity assumptions are made. For multi-sector planning, it is an open issue whether useful results can be obtained by ignoring the non-convexities that operate in individual sectors. See Chenery (1959).

all of the numerical results were obtained without the use of electronic computers.

Parts II and III focus upon algorithms and computations, and are addressed to operations researchers. Part II deals with the analytically tractable case—that of a single producing area. Part III deals with the less tractable case of multiple producing areas. It contains results obtained through approximation procedures, relying upon electronic computing equipment. These approximations are crude, and the present volume will have served its purpose if it stimulates others to search for superior algorithms. Preinvestment programming leads to a significant class of practical cases for which we are currently able to formulate numerical models, but not to solve them in a fully rigorous fashion.

REFERENCES

Bellman, R., and S. Dreyfus, *Applied Dynamic Programming*, Princeton University Press, 1962.

Bierwert, D. V., and F. A. Krone, 'How to Find Best Site for New Plant', *Chemical Engineering*, December 1955; reprinted in C. H. Chilton (ed.), *Cost Engineering in the Process Industries*, McGraw-Hill Book Co., Inc., New York, 1960.

Chakravarty, S., and L. Lefeber, 'An Optimizing Planning Model', *The Economic Weekly*, Bombay, February 1965.

Chenery, H. B., 'The Interdependence of Investment Decisions', in M. Abramowitz *et al.*, *The Allocation of Economic Resources*, Stanford University Press, 1959.

Holt, C. C., F. Modigliani, J. F. Muth, and H. A. Simon, *Planning Production, Inventories, and Work Force*, Prentice-Hall, Englewood Cliffs, New Jersey, 1960.

Malinvaud, E., 'Decentralized Procedures for Planning', mimeographed paper, Center for Research in Management Science, University of California, Berkeley, November 1963.

Manne, A. S., 'Capacity Expansion and Probabilistic Growth', *Econometrica*, October 1961.

— and A. Rudra, 'A Consistency Model of India's Fourth Plan', *Sankhya*, 1965.

Perspective Planning Division, Planning Commission, Government of India, *Notes on Perspective of Development, India: 1960–61 to 1975–76*, April 1964.

Planning Commission, Government of India, *The Planning Process*, New Delhi, October 1963.

Savage, L. J., *The Foundations of Statistics*, John Wiley and Sons, New York, 1954.

Srinivasan, T. N., 'A Critique on the Optimising Planning Model', *The Economic Weekly*, Bombay, February 1965.

United Nations, Economic Commission for Latin America, *Manual on Economic Development Projects*, E/CN.12/426/Add. 1/Rev. 1, New York, 1958.

Veinott, A. F., Jr., and H. M. Wagner, 'Optimal Capacity Scheduling', *Operations Research*, July–August 1962.

Ward, B., 'Linear Programming and Soviet Planning', mimeographed paper presented at University of Rochester, New York, May 1965.

CHAPTER 2

CALCULATIONS FOR A SINGLE PRODUCING AREA

ALAN S. MANNE

General considerations

This chapter deals with several of the more tractable versions of the plant size problem. These models are each phrased in terms of meeting a stipulated demand at minimum cost. The first version described is a stationary one; the following two are dynamic problems in which time enters in an essential way. In each instance, we rely upon the simplifying assumption of a single producing area. Since this assumption seems appropriate for analyses such as that of the aluminium industry (Chapter 3 below), it is of practical interest in itself. Moreover, the single area case is an instructive one. It focuses attention upon a qualitative aspect of economies-of-scale: that individual plants must be large and separated from each other by long intervals in time.

With the simplifying assumption of a single area, we can readily consider questions of the following type: (1) What will be the consequences of errors in estimating the demand to be satisfied? (2) What are the consequences of using incorrect shadow prices for the inputs, e.g. too low a cost of capital? (3) What would happen if the demand did not have to be satisfied directly by new production capacity, but could be handled temporarily by alternate high-cost sources of supply? (4) What would be the cost of satisfying the political pressures to build small plants at frequent intervals of time? The single area model is simple enough so that these questions have easy answers. Needless to say, the model cannot itself determine what is the best estimate of demand, of the cost of capital, etc. The model's purpose is to sharpen the issues, and to explore the consequences of alternative parameter values.

The stationary case

In order to motivate much of the discussion that follows, we begin with the stationary, single area case. This may be visualized in terms of a conventional make-or-buy diagram, Figure 2.1. During a specified period of time, there is a certain demand to be met. Two alternatives are to be considered for meeting this demand: internal manufacture (curve M) and outside purchase (curve P). The cost of outside purchase is shown here as strictly proportional to the amount taken—hence as a straight line through the origin. Internal manufacture is supposedly subject to economies-of-scale, and is therefore shown with a concave cost function.

Because of the shape of the functions M and P, the minimum-cost decision is an all-or-none choice. Whenever the demand is estimated as lying to the left of the break-even point X, then outside procurement of the entire demand quantity is optimal. For a demand quantity to the right of X, internal manufacture is less costly.

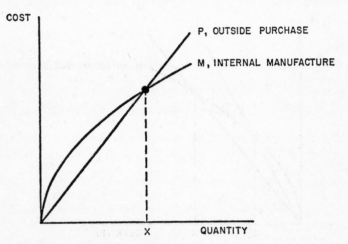

Figure 2.1.—Cost of Internal Manufacture versus Outside Purchase

Before proceeding to more complex cases, this make-or-buy model is helpful because:

(a) The model makes precise what lies behind the notion of a 'minimum economic size unit', a plant that will satisfy a demand of size X. Contrary to much of what is written sloppily on the subject, this minimum size is not determined on technological grounds alone. Relative prices enter also, and these are likely to differ from one nation to another. India cannot afford to assume uncritically that her minimum economic plant size will be the same as it is in Europe, Japan, or the USA.[1]

The overall shortage of foreign exchange in India means that the

[1] International trade journals are replete with rules-of-thumb such as the following pronouncement made after describing the expansion plans of European petrochemical manufacturers, 'Anyone coming on stream in 1964 should plan to produce 100,000 tons per year of ethylene.'

minimum unit size has to be evaluated on the basis of product import prices higher than the official exchange rate.[1] Figure 2.2 indicates that a foreign exchange scarcity will rotate the external purchase curve P upward to P', hence lowering the minimum economic size of a unit from X to X'. A foreign exchange shortage operates in much the same fashion as an increase in transport costs for the imported product. Both constitute barriers to international trade, and both operate so as to reduce the minimum economic unit size.

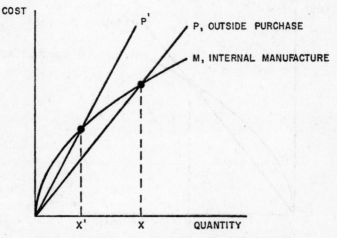

Figure 2.2.—Reduction in Minimum Economic Unit Size

(b) Figure 2.1 will suggest why—even in this trivially simple case—a local optimum is not a global one. We are dealing with concave cost functions. No myopic algorithm (e.g. the differential calculus or linear programming) can be guaranteed to find the optimum.

Let x be the quantity manufactured domestically, y the quantity purchased externally, and D the total demand to be met. The cost per unit of outside purchase is p, and the cost of domestic manufacture is $M(x)$, a *concave* function of x. The make-or-buy problem can then be formulated as:

---

[1] To allow for this foreign exchange consideration, Institut Français du Pétrole (1963, p. 16) concluded that 'India should not, unless there are specific valid overriding reasons, consider producing any petrochemical whose selling price will be more than 130% of what other people in advanced countries pay for the same product'.

$$\text{minimize:} \quad M(x) + p\,y$$
$$\text{subject to:} \quad x + y = D$$
$$x, y \geqslant 0$$

A minimum-cost solution occurs at one or the other extreme point: $x = D$, $y = 0$; or $x = 0$, $y = D$. For $\epsilon > 0$, it is possible that $pD < [M(\epsilon) + p(D - \epsilon)]$, and yet that $pD > M(D)$. A local optimum is not necessarily a global one. For the same reason, it is inappropriate to rely upon the competitive market mechanisms of neoclassical economics.

(c) By revising the interpretation of one label on Figure 2.1, we can explore the logical implications of the innocent-looking assumption that one could manufacture internally and then sell as much as one pleases at the prevailing price on an outside market. As before, the single period's total cost of domestic manufacture will be represented by curve M, implying economies-of-scale. Now, however, the line P is interpreted as the gross revenue obtained by producing and then selling on the outside market. The vertical difference between the cost and revenue curve would represent the area's net profit from the export operation.

This set of plausible assumptions leads to totally implausible conclusions. In order to maximize net profits from exports, the area should manufacture and sell an infinite quantity of product, thereby generating an infinite amount of net profits.

It is in order to eliminate these paradoxes of infinity that we take as a datum the market demand, including possible export quantities. We do not assume that unlimited quantities of product can be sold on an outside market at a fixed price—even though we occasionally assume that unlimited *purchases* are obtainable at a fixed price.

Time discounting

In each of the models to be considered hereafter, time plays an essential role. The costs incurred at one point in time have an influence upon the costs incurred at other points. Under conditions of growing demand and economies-of-scale in plant construction, there will typically be a choice between several time streams of expenditure. If a single large plant is built, advantage can be taken of economies-of-scale in construction. Alternatively, if several smaller plants are built at different points of time, there is the advantage of delaying a portion of the total investment outlays.[1]

[1] Calculations of this general type are described in internal publications of American Telephone and Telegraph Company dating back at least as early as 1945. The models considered here are similar to those of Chenery (1952),

To make comparisons between expenditures incurred at different dates, we shall always use the discounted cash flow (present value) criterion. For intertemporal comparisons, there is no longer much doubt that this has both theoretical and practical advantages over that old-fashioned criterion for decisions: the payout period. For the class of investment problems being considered here, the payout criterion leads to unreasonable implications. E.g. if successive plant investment decisions were guided by a five-year payout rule, this would typically imply that each new plant should cover exactly five years' worth of growth in demand—no matter how great or how small were the economies-of-scale.

Despite widespread agreement that there is some positive rate at which future costs and benefits should be discounted, there is substantial disagreement on the elements relevant to the determination of that rate. For the Indian studies described below, the standard rate used has been 10% per annum. This particular number has some political merit as a compromise between the book-keeping rates of return measured in the public sector (roughly 5%) and in the private sector (roughly 20% before corporate income taxes of 50%). See Lefeber and Datta Chaudhuri (1964, p. 99).

As one line of defence of the 10% rate, there is an economic argument that deserves consideration: one premised upon self-financing within the industrial and public utilities sector of the economy—taking the public and private enterprises as a whole. In the Indian context, self-financing appears far more reasonable than it would in the USA with its extensive private capital markets and its automated methods for ensuring compliance with the tax laws. India's private capital markets are small in relation to the volume of investment funds required for rapid development, and the Government of India has an extremely limited ability to raise additional funds through conventional taxation.

Under the circumstances, there has been a trend in official thinking towards the view that the public as well as the private sector enterprises ought to generate a substantial fraction of the resources required for their own further growth. According to the then Steel Minister, C. Subramanian (1963): 'The raising of part of the capital resources through an element in the price (of the product) is particularly justified when the undertaking involved is in the public sector, and the benefits go back to the community as a whole.' This view is stated even more explicitly in Perspective Planning Division (1964, Appendix K):

McDowell (1960), and Coleman and York (1964). The exposition follows closely that in Manne (1961).

'The greater is the role of the public sector in the development of the country, the greater is its responsibility to provide increasing resources for development out of its productive activities. The present position in this regard leaves much to be desired, and the returns on investments made, for one reason or another continue to be meagre. This, however, cannot be accepted as inevitable. . . . An adequate rate of return on capital must be insisted upon in the interest of the growth of the economy.'

Given self-financing within the industrial and public utilities sectors, and making the further assumption that these advanced sectors have: (1) a constant aggregate capital-output ratio,[1] (2) a planned growth rate in the neighbourhood of 10% per annum, (3) depreciation charges equal to replacement investments, and (4) a reinvestment co-efficient[2] of 100% out of profits, then one comes up with a magic number to be used in investment and pricing decisions: a rate of return equal to the growth rate of 10% per annum. Nothing further will be said here on the subject of rate-of-return. Instead, the reader is referred to the following: von Neumann (1945–46), Solomon (1959), Hufschmidt *et al.* (1961), Massé (1962), Marglin (1963), Hahn and Matthews (1964), and Harberger (1964).

Time horizons

In evaluating alternative investment programmes, the discounted cash flows will have to be summed up over some predetermined time horizon, say over 25 years, 100 years, or over an infinite span of time. The question that naturally arises is this: Our immediate decisions refer only to those investments that have to be made over the next 5–10 years. Why be concerned with an horizon of 25 or more years when it is so difficult to forecast technological developments, costs, and demand patterns over such a long period?

For the purpose of these studies, a time horizon of ten years or less would be distinctly unsatisfactory. A fixed ten-year horizon rules out many of the alternative plant sizes which would otherwise be reasonable to consider. With any monotone increasing cost function, this horizon would eliminate sizes that cover more than ten

[1] Stephen Marglin, the earliest reader of this paper, has objected to supposing simultaneously that the advanced sectors have a constant *ex ante* capital-output ratio and yet that there are alternative techniques of production (alternate plant sizes, locations, etc.) available to the individual sectors.

[2] What is really being assumed is that any corporate taxes and dividends paid out are exactly offset by the inflow of new private and public capital to these enterprises, taken as a group.

C

years' worth of growth in demand. Moreover, if we were to build a series of plants at equidistant time intervals (following a policy of constant cycle time), the horizon of one decade would restrict us to the following intervals: $10 \cdot 0$ years or $5 \cdot 0$ or $3 \cdot 3$ or $2 \cdot 5$ or.... Within this harmonic series, there is no possibility of choosing a time interval of $4 \cdot 0$ or $6 \cdot 0$ years between successive plants—although both of these intervals would fit in if the horizon were lengthened slightly from 10 to 12 years.

The harmonic series restriction is not at all inherent in the technology of plant construction, and seems irrelevant for purposes of economic evaluation. This is a significant argument in favour of postulating an infinite time horizon. No restrictions upon the plant size are then imposed by the horizon itself. For models such as those considered in Part I of this volume, it works out that computations are more convenient with an infinite than with a finite horizon. For other models, the reverse is true. E.g. in Part III below, with multiple producing areas, it was convenient to idealize time in discrete periods of a single year, and to consider time horizons of 24 years. For this time span, the constant cycle time restriction implies successive plants built at intervals of either 1, 2, 3, 4, 6, 8, 12 or 24 years.

A dynamic case—arithmetic growth of demand—no imports

In this simplest of dynamic models, it is assumed that our single producing area is to serve a demand that grows at a continuous arithmetic rate over time. There are to be no imports into the market area served, and all demand is to be satisfied by internal production. The discount rate and the manufacturing cost functions remain stationary over time, the plant life is infinite, and the horizon is infinite.

With these assumptions, it turns out that the optimal policy consists of building successive plants of the same size at equidistant intervals of time. Figures 2.3a and 2.3b will help the reader to visualize why this policy of constant cycle time is optimal. At time 0, the annual rate of demand is D_0. Thereafter, demand grows at a constant annual increment D. The time series of demand is shown as the solid line in Figure 2.3a, and the dotted line indicates the cumulative installed manufacturing capacity. A new plant is installed at time 0, another at time x, another at $2x$, . . . Thus, the installed capacity follows a staircase pattern—never dropping below the solid line, i.e. never failing to satisfy the demand.

Another way of looking at this same process is shown in Figure

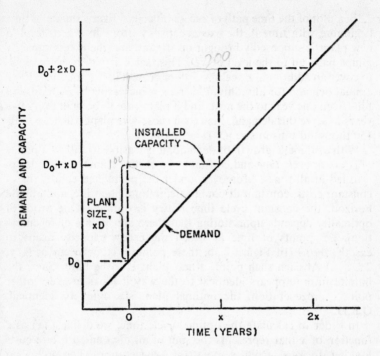

Figure 2.3a.—Time Paths of Demand and Installed Capacity

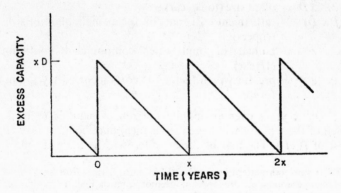

Figure 2.3b.—Time Path of Excess Capacity

2.3b, a plot of the time path of excess capacity.[1] Every x units of time beginning with time 0, the excess capacity drops to a zero level, a new plant is supposedly brought on stream, and the excess capacity jumps back up to the level of xD. This new capacity is just enough to cover an additional x years' worth of growth in demand. E.g. if the annual demand for aluminium in India is increasing by 30 thousand tons from one year to the next, and if plants are to be built every five years to serve this demand, then each successive plant will have to be 150 thousand tons in size. ($x D = 5(30)$).

With arithmetic growth of demand, it is feasible to follow a policy of *constant cycle time* and constant size of new plants. Demands are satisfied at all times. Moreover, under the postulated conditions of constant costs, constant discount rate, infinite plant life, and infinite horizon, the constant cycle time policy is optimal. One proof of optimality depends upon noting that there are 'points of regeneration', i.e. points of time at which the excess capacity drops to exactly zero.[2] (In Figure 2.3b, these points of time occur at 0, x, $2x$, . . .) At each such point, a new plant is to be built. Since the infinite future appears identical to the way it looks at every other point of regeneration, the optimal plant size must be identical. Q.E.D.

In order to calculate the optimal cycle time, we define $C(x)$ as a function of x that represents the sum of all discounted future costs looking forward from a point of regeneration. The following additional definitions are employed:

Let D = annual increase in demand (tons/year)/year
$\quad\ x$ = time interval between successive plants (years)
$\therefore\ xD$ = plant size (tons/year)
$f(x D)$ = investment cost function for a single plant of size xD (rupees)
$\quad\ r$ = annual discount rate, compounded continuously (1/year)
$\therefore\ e^{-rt}$ = present worth factor for costs incurred t years in the future

Every x years over an infinite horizon, a plant is to be built. Each of these plants will have the identical undiscounted investment cost of $f(xD)$. The first of these plants is to be built at time zero,

---

[1] The sawtooth pattern in Figure 2.3b brings out the direct analogy to the stationary economic lot size model of inventory control. For an exposition of this inventory model, see Whitin (1957).

[2] For a similar application of the idea of regeneration points, see Karlin (1958, pp. 280–85).

the second at time x, etc. Then since $C(x)$ is defined as a function of x that represents the sum of all discounted future costs looking forward from a point of regeneration, the following recursive equation may be written down:

$$C(x) = f(xD) + e^{-rx} C(x) \qquad (2.1)$$

The first term on the right-hand side indicates the investment costs incurred directly at the beginning of the first cycle. The second term measures the sum of all installation costs incurred in subsequent cycles, and discounts these from the next point of regeneration back to the present one, a difference of x years. From (2.1), it follows directly that:

$$C(x) = \frac{f(xD)}{1 - e^{-rx}} \qquad (2.2)$$

Numerical results may be obtained by replacing the general function $f(xD)$ by a specific one that is popular in the engineering literature for such process industries as chemicals, cement, petroleum, electricity generation, and primary metals:

$$f(xD) = k \cdot (x D)^a \qquad (2.3)$$

where k is a constant of proportionality. It may be shown that the exponent a measures the ratio of the incremental to the average costs of a unit of plant capacity.

If the exponent $a = 0 \cdot 6$, the cost equation (2.3) would represent the 'six-tenths rule' for scaling of costs.[1] With $a = 0 \cdot 6$, there are significant economies-of-scale. Doubling the plant size will result in an increase of 52% in the investment cost. With $a = 1 \cdot 0$, there are no longer any economies-of-scale. Doubling the plant size will increase the investment cost by 100%. Hereafter, the following restriction is placed upon the economies-of-scale parameter a:

$$0 < a < 1 \cdot 0 \qquad (2.4)$$

Substituting (2.3) into (2.2), we now have the cost equation to be minimized with respect to the cycle time x:

$$C(x) = \frac{k \cdot (x D)^a}{1 - e^{-rx}} \qquad (2.5)$$

[1] After reviewing data for 36 types of chemical, petroleum, and primary metal plants, Chilton (1960, p. 284) says: 'Can we conclude, based on this evidence, that costs of complete process plants follow the six-tenths rule? Can this rule be safely employed in economic studies based on pre-design cost estimates? The writer believes we can answer yes to both questions.'

Note that four numerical parameters (k, D, a and r) enter into equation (2.4), but that the optimal value of the cycle time x^* is independent of the cost constant k and of the annual increment in demand, D. The two other parameters a and r do affect the optimal value x^*, and a cross-plot is presented in Figure 2.4.[1]

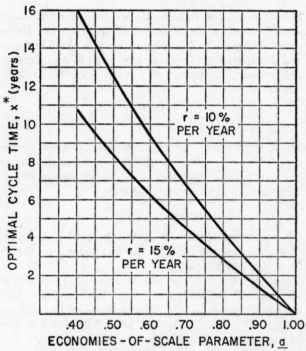

Figure 2.4.—Cross-Plot for Optimal Cycle Time

[1] Figure 2.4 may be calculated by taking logarithms of both sides of (2.5), differentiating the logarithms and setting the results equal to zero:

$$\frac{d \log C(x)}{dx} = \frac{a}{x} - \frac{r}{e^{rx} - 1} = 0$$

$$\therefore a = \frac{rx^*}{e^{rx^*} - 1}$$

For positive values of x and r note that these equations may be solved if and only if the parameter a satisfies the restriction (2.4): $0 < a < 1$.

The cost function (2.5) has a unique minimum with respect to x. This may be proved by noting that the function is continuous and differentiable for all positive values of x, that the function tends toward infinity as x tends towards either zero or infinity, and that there is a single point for which the derivative of $\log C(x)$ is zero.

For the Indian industries studied, the typical values for a and r would be $0 \cdot 70$ and 10% per year respectively. These values imply that $x^* = 6 \cdot 75$ years. The higher the discount rate and the less significant the economies-of-scale, the less will it pay to build capacity ahead of demand.

Some questions about the model

This analysis is all quite tidy as far as it goes, but there are several questions that will immediately suggest themselves to a practical decision-maker:

(*a*) *Question*. Why have the operating costs for fuel, raw materials, and labour been omitted from the cost function (2.5)?

Answer. Typically, these operating costs are considered proportional to the output at each plant. Typically, it is also supposed that the combined output from all plants is equal to the total demand target for each future point of time. The total physical quantity of each proportional input is therefore fixed by the demand target—independent of the plant sizes or locations chosen. Hence, in problems involving a single producing location—or when all locations purchase their inputs at identical unit prices—the combined value of these inputs is a fixed charge, and may be omitted from the criterion for optimization of plant size, location and time-phasing. Of course, if there are any regional variations in the input prices or if there are any economies-of-scale associated with the operating costs (e.g. wages, salaries and overheads), these elements must be introduced into the cost function.

(*b*) *Question*. In realistic situations, the plant life is not infinite. How is the analysis then modified?

Answer. The assumption of infinite life is made for analytical convenience so that each point of regeneration (zero excess capacity) is identical with the others. For a finite plant life, (say t years), replacement costs may be included through multiplying the original investment costs by a replacement factor ρ—as though these original costs were incurred every t years over an infinite horizon.[1] The replacement factor is defined as the sum of a geometric series of one unit of costs incurred every t years, discounting at the annual rate of r:

---

[1] For a finite plant life, the policy of constant cycle time and constant plant size is no longer guaranteed to be optimal. It is, however, a feasible policy. Since the replacement factor (2.6) does not grossly exceed unity for the plant lives and discount rates that are of immediate relevance, we have not investigated any further into the consequences of the finite life assumption.

Replacement factor $= 1 + e^{-rt} + e^{-2rt} + e^{-3rt} + \ldots$

$$\rho = \frac{1}{1 - e^{-rt}} \quad \ldots \ldots \quad (2.6)$$

Example: For a discount rate $r = 10\%$ per year and a service life $t = 18$ years, the replacement factor $= 1 \cdot 20$. These parameters imply that the overwhelming majority of costs are associated with the first unit constructed. The present value of all the remaining plants in the infinite sequence of replacements is only 20% that of the first unit.[1]

(c) *Question.* What provision has been made for taxes?

Answer. None. From an economy-wide viewpoint, taxes are not real economic costs but transfer payments to the Government. Presumably, India's investment licensing decisions are to be made upon the basis of social rather than private costs.

For similar reasons, there is no distinction made here between the return on debt and the return on equity capital. Through appropriate leverage (the ratio of debt to total capital), it can be arranged so that equity shareholders receive 10% or more in after-tax return on their investment, even when the earnings of the enterprise are restricted to 10% on total capital investment before payment of a 50% corporate income tax. This result would take place if, say, the enterprise had a capital structure with 2/3 debt paying 5% annual interest, and if the 1/3 equity earned 10% after taxes (20% pretax). This high a debt ratio for a manufacturing enterprise—though rare in the USA—would not be uncommon in India.

(d) *Question.* What is the meaning of the term 'plant size', and how does this fit in with the licensing authorities' definitions of 'new unit' and 'substantial expansion'?

Answer. As used in the engineering cost estimation literature, the term 'plant size' usually refers to a balanced plant built at a single point of time. In actual practice, it is seldom that a completely balanced expansion takes place. In the cement industry (Chapter 6) the investment required for a 'new unit' would probably include a

---

[1] The replacement factor is closely related to the capital recovery factor (c.r.f.) utilized in engineering economy calculations. (See Grant and Ireson (1960, p. 45).) The c.r.f. represents an annual stream of capital charges, and the replacement factor ρ equals the present value of those annual charges summed over an infinite horizon. Example: For $r = 10\%$ and $t = 18$, the annual c.r.f. $= (0 \cdot 10)$ $(1 \cdot 20) = (r)(\rho) = 12\%$ annual charges.

Both the c.r.f. and the replacement factor imply annual capital charges considerably *below* the conventional level consisting of straight-line depreciation plus yield on the undepreciated initial capital. The latter would amount to $(1/18) + 10\% = 15 \cdot 6\%$ annual charges on the initial capital.

single rotary kiln, but might also include sufficient provision in ancillary units (e.g. the slurry basin and the smokestack) to serve a second rotary kiln when and if it gets constructed. For cement plants, our calculations allow explicitly for the distinction between a 'new unit' and a 'substantial expansion'. In the other industries, the data were not available to support this particular refinement. For these other cases, it was assumed that the entire ultimate investment cost for a balanced plant is incurred at the time the plant is first brought on stream.

(e) *Question.* From the viewpoint of equipment supply and maintenance, it is usually desirable to standardize the alternative plant sizes. What provision is made for this?

Answer. If there are just a few predetermined plant sizes available to an industry, the selection from within this set may be made through equation (2.2). The constant cycle time result is not based upon any restriction that the plant size be either a continuous or a discrete variable.

For each of the four industries studied, we have attempted to pose the problem of standardization in a reverse form: Given the costs and the regional patterns of growth in demand, what would be the best set of standard plant sizes? In order to answer this in a fully satisfactory fashion, information is needed from the equipment-supplying industries on *their* economies-of-scale. Some clues may be obtained, however, from an analysis confined to the equipment-using industry.

(f) *Question.* Why is it assumed that demand grows at a steady arithmetic rate? Most Indian demand forecasts are based upon constant geometric rates of growth.

Answer. The arithmetic growth assumption is made both for the sake of convenience in computations and also because of doubts that geometric growth rates of 10–15% per annum can be extrapolated into the indefinite future. T. N. Srinivasan (Chapter 9 below) has studied a case in which the single producing area is required to satisfy demands that are growing geometrically. When investment costs are described through the power function (2.3), he shows that the policy of constant cycle time is again optimal. His calculations also suggest that if the arithmetic growth model indicates that it is optimal to instal a plant to cover x^* years' worth of growth, this plant size will be approximately correct for the *first* installation to satisfy a geometric growth curve—provided that the annual average growth is the same over the first x^* years. This approximate result does not apply when the demand growth rate takes on bizarre values, e.g. 50% per annum compounded over the indefinite future.

Chapter 11 below deals with the case in which a single producing area is to meet an arbitrarily increasing time path of demand, one other than arithmetic or geometric growth. For this situation, constant cycle time policies are no longer optimal, but nevertheless there is an efficient computational procedure for obtaining an optimal policy. This method is again based on 'points of regeneration'.

(g) *Question.* Often, the availability of a new source of supply will stimulate additional demand for the product. Is this effect considered?

Answer. No, this was not done. Supply does create its own demand—particularly under conditions of repressed inflation as in India. This would, however, be extremely difficult to estimate quantitatively. By ignoring this effect, the calculations have probably been biased in favour of small-scale plants.

(h) *Question.* What happens in the case of a process that generates several co-products?

Answer. For one such example, see Chapter 5 below. This deals with the case of a main product, caustic soda, associated with two co-products, chlorine and hydrogen. Another similar case was investigated but is not reported in detail here. The process consisted of naphtha steam cracking to produce a main product of ethylene (a yield of approximately 30% by weight of the initial feedstock), together with co-products of propylene, butylenes, cracked naphtha, and fuel gases.[1] It appeared plausible to suppose that the size of the steam cracker would be determined by the growth of demand for the main product ethylene, and that there would be sufficient market demand within India to absorb the co-products at a constant unit realization. This meant that the co-products did not enter into the calculation of optimal size for the cracking unit. Their only effect was to provide a by-product credit, a reduction in the operating costs per unit of ethylene production.

A dynamic case—arithmetic growth of demand—time-phased imports

Just as in the previous dynamic model, we assume that the single producing area is to serve a demand that grows at a continuous arithmetic rate over time; the discount rate and the manufacturing cost functions remain stationary; the plant life and the time horizon are infinite. Now, however, it is assumed that the area's demands may be satisfied through imports, a high-cost temporary means of deferring the investment in internal production capacity until a date when the domestic demand grows sufficiently to justify a new

---

[1] For suggesting this problem, the author is indebted to Lavraj Kumar, Senior Industrial Adviser (Petrochemicals), Directorate General of Technical Development.

plant.[1] (Alternately this process can be viewed in terms of backlogging the internal demand and paying a penalty per unit of backlog.) Just as in the stationary make-or-buy example (curve P in Figure 2.1 above), the penalty costs per unit of outside purchase will be assumed constant, independent of the volume of imports.

Figure 2.5 will help to visualize the relationship between this process and the zero import case shown previously in Figure 2.3b. Just as in the earlier case, we assume that demand grows linearly at

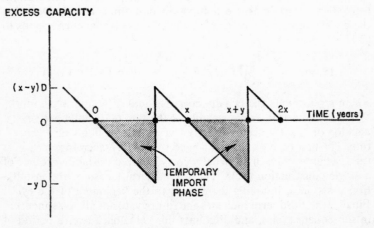

Figure 2.5.—Time Path of Excess Capacity; Time-Phased Imports

the rate of D physical units per year. Again, x years will denote the time interval between each successive installation, and the points $0, x, 2x, \ldots$ still mark the points of regeneration: the points at which excess capacity has just been wiped out. The entire difference between this and the earlier case is that excess capacity is allowed to become negative here, and that demands are temporarily backlogged or satisfied through imports.

Figure 2.5 is drawn on the assumption that y years after a point

[1] The calculations could also be modified to take account of one practice which is being introduced in response to the rationing of foreign exchange. Prior to the construction of a domestic plant, a foreign collaborator 'lends' a specified quantity of the product to an Indian enterprise. Once the plant goes on stream, and while the domestic demand is still below the plant's capacity, the foreign collaborator's commodity loan is repaid with interest—in kind. Through this barter device, no foreign exchange (aside from shipping costs) is either spent or earned by India. This practice is intended only as a temporary means of satisfying current demands by borrowing against the capacity that will be built in the near future.

of regeneration, a new facility is built. The new facility is to cover the increment in demand over a period of x years. Just prior to the on-stream date of the new plant, the excess capacity is $-yD$, a negative quantity. Immediately after this date, the excess capacity rises to $(x - y)D$, a non-negative quantity. We now have two decision variables: x, the interval between two successive installations, and y, the duration of the temporary import phase of each cycle.

Looking forward into the future from a point of regeneration, total discounted costs are a function of both x and y. Denoting these discounted costs by $C(x, y)$, the expression that corresponds to (2.1) is as follows:

$$C(x, y) = \int_{t=0}^{y} p(tD)e^{-rt}dt + e^{-ry}f(xD) + e^{-rx}C(x, y) \quad (2.7)$$

where p represents the penalty costs per unit of temporary imports. When demand is growing steadily at the rate of D units per year, a backlog of size tD occurs exactly t years after a point of regeneration. The first term on the right-hand side of (2.7) therefore measures the discounted sum of all penalty costs incurred during the course of a single construction cycle. The second term measures the installation costs, and discounts them back to the beginning of the cycle. Finally, the third term indicates the future value of all costs incurred in subsequent cycles, and discounts this value back over a period of x years to the initial point of regeneration. After rearranging terms, we obtain:

$$C(x, y) = \frac{\int_{t=0}^{y} p(tD)e^{-rt}dt + e^{-ry}f(xD)}{1 - e^{-rx}} \quad (2.8)$$

A detailed analysis of the cost function (2.8) is to be found in Chapter 10 below by Donald Erlenkotter. The principal results obtained may be stated as follows:

(1) Let x^* and y^* denote optimal values of x and y respectively. A necessary condition for optimality is as follows:

$$y^* = \frac{rf(x^*D)}{pD} \quad . \quad . \quad . \quad . \quad . \quad (2.9)$$

Through (2.9), the problem of optimization is reduced to one involving the single decision variable x, rather than the two variables x and y. Note that y^* vanishes only when p (the unit penalty cost) becomes infinite.

(2) The quantity $(x^* - y^*)$ is always non-negative. Hence, immediately after a new plant is constructed, the amount of excess capacity is non-negative. It follows that a point of regeneration is reached during each cycle. This result needs to be proved here—unlike the zero import case where it is immediately obvious.

(3) For an infinite value of the penalty factor p, the optimal plant size (x^*D) reaches its lowest level. As p decreases, the optimal plant size increases. Temporary imports make it economical to build larger individual plants.

At the end of Chapter 10, tables are provided so that x^* and y^* can be determined numerically for the specific investment cost function (2.3)—given the values of a, r and k/p. The tables are based upon a normalization of physical units so that the demand increment $D = 1\cdot0$. As a result of this normalization, x^*, the optimal time interval between successive plants, is the same number as x^*D, the optimal capacity increment.

Example 1: Let $a = 0\cdot70$ and $r = 10\%$. Then when the penalty factor is infinite ($k/p = 0$), the optimal values are: $x^* = 6\cdot75$ years and $y^* = 0\cdot00$ years. (These results are the same as obtained from the 10% curve in Figure 2.4.) If the penalty factor is lowered so that $k/p = 12\cdot0$, then $x^* = 13\cdot52$ years, and $y^* = 7\cdot43$ years.

Example 2: In Institut Français du Pétrole (1963, p. 18), the Indian programme for new petrochemical plants is described as follows: 'The units will probably start up at 50% or slightly more of capacity and build up over a 3-year period to 100%, or rather more if possible.' In terms of our model, this statement implies that $x = 6$ years, and $y = 3$ years. From the tables in Chapter 10, it can be seen that this Indian petrochemical policy would be approximately optimal for the following combination of parameter values: $a = 0\cdot70$, $r = 20\%$ and $k/p = 4\cdot00$.

Effect of parameter errors and of political constraints

Even these simple models for a single producing area require a considerable input of numerical data: cost functions, demand projections, penalty factors, and a discount rate. Given the uncertainty in choosing each of these, it is prudent to be concerned with the effect of taking decisions on the basis of incorrect parameter estimates. Sensitivity to incorrect parameters—and also to political constraints—will be illustrated through the parameter values used in Example 1, immediately above: $a = 0\cdot70$, $r = 10\%$, $k/p = 0$. It then follows that $x^* = 6\cdot75$ and $y^* = 0\cdot0$.

With these numbers, Figure 2.6 shows the cost consequences of setting the cycle time variable x at values other than the optimal one of 6·75 years. Within a wide range—say from 4 to 8 years—there is hardly any perceptible increase in costs that results from a non-optimal choice of x.

Now suppose the demand forecasters are congenitally optimistic, and that they persistently forecast the annual demand increment D at twice its true value. Although unduly optimistic with respect to

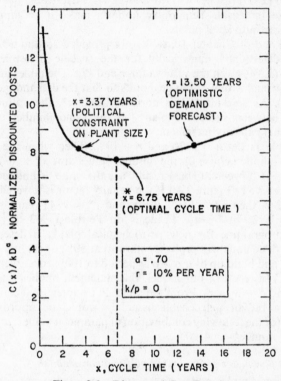

Figure 2.6.—Discounted Cost Function

demand growth, the analysts perform their plant size optimization with the correct values for the discount rate r and the economies-of-scale parameter a. The cycle time variable x is therefore recommended as 6·75 years. However, since the growth parameter D is estimated at twice its actual value, the physical plant size recommendations (xD) are persistently twice the value that is in fact optimal. The over-estimate of D leads to an actual cycle time of 13·50 rather than 6·75 years. The bias in estimating the demand growth parameter therefore leads to an increase in costs over the minimum attainable level. From Figure 2·6, it can be seen, however, that the resulting cost increase is not disastrous. The parameter error leads to a 7·7% increase over the minimum attainable level of discounted costs over the infinite horizon. The relative error in costs is far smaller than that in the demand growth forecast.

The tables appended to Chapter 10 include information on cost sensitivity. They tabulate the percentage increase in costs that will be associated with setting the cycle time variable x at both half and at twice its optimal value. For the illustrative numerical parameters used in constructing Figure 2.6, the tables show these cost increases as 5·5 and 7·7% for under- and over-shooting respectively.

Departures from the optimal cycle time may result from political considerations as well as from incorrect parameter estimates. In India, it is often considered desirable to build a large number of individual plants in order to spread industrialization over as many states as possible. Now if it is believed expedient to build twice as many individual plants as are economically optimal, this is logically equivalent to choosing a cycle time of 3·37 rather than the optimal value of 6·75 years between plants. Both Figure 2·6 and the tables in Chapter 10 indicate that this results in a cost increase of 5·5%. Unlike a forecasting error, this increase in costs is avoidable. It is important that the decision-makers be presented explicitly with an estimate of the economic loss being imposed deliberately for non-economic reasons.

REFERENCES

Chenery, H., 'Overcapacity and the Acceleration Principle', *Econometrica*, January 1952.

Chilton, C. H., ' "Six-Tenths Factor" Applies to Complete Plant Costs', *Chemical Engineering*, April 1950, reprinted in C. H. Chilton (ed.), *Cost Engineering in the Process Industries*, McGraw-Hill Book Co., Inc., New York, 1960.

Coleman, J. R., Jr., and R. York, 'Optimum Plant Design for a Growing Market', *Industrial and Engineering Chemistry*, January 1964.

Grant, E. L., and W. G. Ireson, *Principles of Engineering Economy*, The Ronald Press Company, New York, 1960.

Hahn, R. F., and R. C. O. Matthews,' The Theory of Economic Growth: A Survey', *The Economic Journal*, December 1964.

Harberger, A. C., 'Techniques of Project Appraisal', Conference on Economic Planning, National Bureau of Economic Research, New York, (preliminary mimeographed paper), November 1964.

Hufschmidt, M. M., J. Krutilla, J. Margolis, and S. A. Marglin, *Standards and Criteria for Formulating and Evaluating Federal Water Resources*

Developments, Report of Panel of Consultants to the Bureau of the Budget, Washington, D.C., June 1961.

Institut Français du Pétrole, *Petrochemical Study for India, Executive Summary*, unpublished document, February 1963.

Karlin, S., 'Application of Renewal Theory to the Study of Inventory Policies', Ch. 15 in K. J. Arrow, S. Karlin, and H. Scarf, *Studies in the Mathematical Theory of Inventory and Production*, Stanford University Press, 1958.

Lefeber, L., and M. Datta Chaudhuri, 'Transportation Policy in India'; Ch. 5 in P. N. Rosenstein-Rodan (ed.), *Pricing and Fiscal Policies*, George Allen and Unwin Ltd., London, 1964.

Manne, A. S., 'Capacity Expansion and Probabilistic Growth', *Econometrica*, October 1961.

McDowell, I., 'The Economical Planning Period for Engineering Works', *Operations Research*, July–August 1960.

Marglin, S. A., 'The Social Rate of Discount and the Optimal Rate of Saving', *Quarterly Journal of Economics*, February 1963.

Massé, P., *Optimal Investment Decisions: Rules for Action and Criteria for Choice*, Prentice-Hall, Inc., Englewood Cliffs, New Jersey, 1962.

Neumann, J. von, 'A Model of General Equilibrium', *Review of Economic Studies*, 1945–46.

Perspective Planning Division, Planning Commission, Government of India, *Notes on Perspective of Development, India: 1960–61 to 1975–76*, April 1964.

Solomon, E. (ed.), *The Management of Corporate Capital*, The Free Press, Glencoe, Illinois, 1959.

Subramanian, C., Inaugural Speech at the Seminar on Public Enterprises, Osmania University, Hyderabad, (mimeographed paper), December 1963.

Whitin, T. M., *The Theory of Inventory Management*, Princeton University Press, Princeton, 1957.

CHAPTER 3

THE ALUMINIUM INDUSTRY

ALAN S. MANNE*

Summary

This chapter begins by outlining the basic data utilized in our study of the aluminium industry: demand forecasts, proportional inputs per unit of output, investment costs, and import prices. The following are the principal policy recommendations:

(1) There are significant economies-of-scale in the construction of aluminium plants. Even allowing for the extra costs of building capacity in advance of demand, it would be worthwhile to construct larger plants than are currently contemplated. If India intends to remain self-sufficient in aluminium at all times in the future, a plant size of 100–150 thousand tons would be less expensive than individual stages of 25–30 thousand tons, as recommended in a report of the sub-group for this industry.

(2) If India is willing to plan on purchasing imported aluminium at specific phases of her future construction programme, there can be a saving as compared with a policy of self-sufficiency. Imports permit a saving regardless of whether one employs the official exchange rate or a shadow price of 50% above this rate. Incidentally, with a policy of planned temporary imports, there is an even stronger economic case in favour of large-sized plants.

(3) For each annual ton of metal output in an integrated alumina and aluminium smelter unit, it takes approximately three kilowatts of installed electric power capacity (operated year-round at an 80% factor). A large smelter, say 100–150 thousand tons/year, would imply a large block of uncommitted electric power: 300–450 installed megawatts. This consideration should not impose a serious restriction upon the maximum size of a smelter—*provided* that the aluminium commitment is planned simultaneously with a major power project.

Demand forecasts

In predicting future demand for aluminium ingots, the estimates have been taken over directly from two sources: Perspective Planning

* The author is indebted to Donald Erlenkotter, P. N. Radhakrishnan, and T. V. S. Rao for their assistance.

D

Division (1964) and Sub-group Report (1964).[1] On the basis of material balances and end-use analysis, the two sources agree roughly as follows:[1]

To simplify the analysis, it is supposed here that demands will keep on increasing over the indefinite future at the constant *arithmetic* growth rate of 30 thousand tons/year.[2] The model chooses (at least on paper) a plant size so as to meet these future demands at minimum discounted cost.

The model is phrased in terms of meeting the future *national* demands at minimum cost—without regard to details of where the producing and consuming centres will be located. That is, for calculating an optimal plant size, it is supposed that the producing locations will all be oriented towards low-cost sources of power and of bauxite, rather than towards the major centres of consumption. The following rough numbers tend to confirm this viewpoint. They suggest that transport costs on the finished product would not be a significant enough element to warrant market-oriented aluminium smelters in India, and that all of India may be idealized as a single producing area:

Upper bound on rail transport cost—shipping cost at a distance of 1,400 kilometres between point of production and of consumption (Bombay–Madras distance is only 1,280 kilometres)	Rs. 119 per ton of ingots
Electric power cost at Rs. 200/kw. year = Rs. 0·0228/kwhr (regional differences in cost could easily exceed Rs. 0·0100/kwhr)	Rs. 480 per ton of ingots
Ex-factory price of aluminium ingots	Rs. 3,000 per ton of ingots

---

[1] The exact reference to the Sub-group is as follows: Sub-group for Aluminium, Magnesium and Silicon of the Planning Group for Non-Ferrous Metals Industry.

Both sources agree in supposing that by 1970–71 India will become self-sufficient in aluminium ingots. In Table C-31, Perspective Planning Division (1964), imports are also shown as zero for 1975–76. For purposes of calculating an optimal plant size, two alternatives are investigated below with respect to imports: self-sufficiency at all times versus a policy of planned temporary imports during specific phases of the industry's future construction programme.

	Domestic production of aluminium ingots
1965–66	70 thousand metric tons/year
1970–71	240 thousand metric tons/year
Average annual increment in output over Fourth Plan (in round numbers)	30 thousand metric tons/year

[2] Alternatively, if one wishes to work out the implications of a constant *geometric* rate of demand growth, there is available the approach suggested by T. N. Srinivasan in chapter 9 of this volume.

Raw materials, power and other proportional costs

Table 3.1 summarizes the viewpoint taken with respect to those inputs *not* subject to economies-of-scale. These proportional operating costs—which include all elements but capital charges—add up to Rs. 1,720 per ton of ingots.

By assuming that each of the elements in Table 3.1 is proportional to output, the results are undoubtedly biased in favour of small-size plants. If an aluminium smelter were vertically integrated with the production of bauxite, electric power, and/or caustic soda, there is every reason to believe that the cost of these inputs would be subject to economies-of-scale.

Small plants have also been given the benefit of the doubt in the case of labour, maintenance and overhead charges. Here—for want of more precise data—we have valued these items at 50% of the inputs

TABLE 3.1

*Operating costs proportional to output of metal;
alumina plant integrated with smelter*

Raw materials, power and fuel	Physical inputs per ton of metal output*†	Approximate price per physical unit of input	Value of inputs per ton of metal output
		Rs.	Rs.
Bauxite	5·50 tons	30	165
Electric power	21 thousand kwhrs	22·8	480
Coal (10,000 B.T.U./lb.)	1·5 tons	20	30
Caustic soda	0·20 tons	700	140
Fuel oil	0·32 tons	140	45
Lime	0·10 tons	25	3
Petroleum coke	0·45 tons	250	112
Cryolite	0·05 tons	1,200	60
Aluminium fluoride	0·03 tons	1,200	36
Pitch	0·19 tons	400	76

Sub-total Rs. 1,147

Labour, maintenance, establishment and overheads
50% of sub-total for raw materials, power and fuel   Rs.   573

Proportional operating costs   Rs. 1,720

NOTES: * Throughout this volume, the unit 'ton' refers to a metric ton.
† Source for physical inputs: Sub-group Report (1964).

of raw materials, power and fuel. (This 50% factor is based upon an estimate in Tariff Commission (1960, pp. 20, 21) on costs at the Hirakud smelter, Indian Aluminium Company. At that time the Hirakud smelter had an annual ingot capacity of only 10,000 tons.)

Investment costs

For economies-of-scale in investment costs, two sources were available: Reimers (1963) and Sub-group Report (1964). Both give separate estimates for alumina and for aluminium smelters.[1] For alumina, the two estimates virtually coincide. For the smelter stage, however, there is a significant discrepancy between the two estimates of investment cost per ton of annual metal capacity. (See Figure 3.1.)

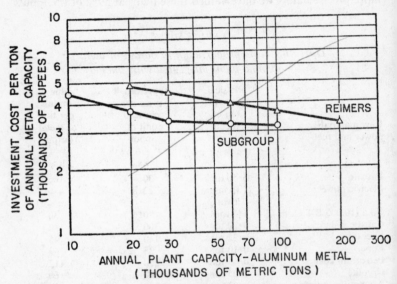

Figure 3.1.—Investment Costs —Aluminium Smelter—Self-Baking Anodes

The Sub-group curve shows a distinct 'knee' at 30 thousand tons of capacity, whereas the Reimers curve keeps dropping log-linearly over the entire range up to 200 thousand tons.

Evidently the plant size implications of these two curves are altogether different. On the basis of its curve, the Sub-group recom-

[1] All smelters considered here have Soderberg self-baking anodes. (There would be slightly greater economies-of-scale with prebaked anodes.) The alumina plants are estimated on the basis of trihydrate bauxite.

mends as follows, (p. 8): ' . . . a 50/60 thousand tonne per annum capacity plant would be a reasonable sized unit for Indian conditions and this could be obtained in two stages starting with the minimum of about 25/30 thousand tonnes.'[1]

Our reason for preferring Reimers' estimates—hence favouring larger-sized plants—is this: The Sub-group's curve is based upon the use of 50,000 ampere pots at all levels of capacity. On the other hand, Reimers takes account of the realistic possibility of employing higher amperages at higher plant capacity levels. This is a seemingly detailed technical issue and undoubtedly deserves further investigation. The issue appears crucial to the question of optimal smelter plant size.

For better or worse, pending further investigation, we have adopted Reimers' estimates. Expressing his curves algebraically[2] in terms of the symbols used in the preceding chapter, the economies-of-scale parameter $a = 0.77$. That is:

Let x = time interval between successive plants (years)

Let D = 30 = annual increase in metal demand (thousands of tons); from p. 50 above

$\therefore xD$ = $30x$ = plant size (thousands of tons)

Let $f(xD)$ = initial investment cost for building a single plant of size x (millions of Rs.)

Let k = constant of proportionality

$\therefore f(x)$ = $k(xD)^{0.77} = 197 x^{0.77}$ (millions of Rs.).   (3.1)

NOTE: It is hazardous to extrapolate (3.1) to values of x above 6.67 years. (With demand increasing at the annual rate of 30, this cycle time is equivalent to a 200 thousand ton plant.)

Optimal plant size—self-sufficiency constraint

Now that the proportional operating costs and the initial investment costs have been estimated, it is possible to apply the model outlined in Chapter 2 for a single producing area. Cost equation (3.2) follows from the assumption of self-sufficiency. That is, at each point of time

[1] Both curves on Figure 3.1 apparently refer to a plant built in a single stage. Separate data are not available on 'substantial expansions' versus 'new units'. On this subject, Reimers remarks as follows: 'In general the cost of additional potlines is from two-thirds to three-quarters of the cost of a new plant.' p. 28.

[2] No additional allowance is made here for *replacement* of the initial plant. E.g. with a 10% discount rate and a 24-year life, a replacement allowance would have the effect of multiplying $f(x)$ by a constant factor of 1.10 at all levels of capacity. (See equation (2.6) in Chapter 2.) This constant factor has been omitted here because there is some evidence that Reimers has slightly overstated the absolute level of investment costs under Indian conditions.

in the future t, India's domestic aluminium production capacity is constrained to be equal to or greater than the domestic demand tD:

$$\begin{bmatrix} \text{total dis-} \\ \text{counted costs} \\ \text{over the} \\ \text{indefinite} \\ \text{future (Rs.} \\ \text{millions)} \end{bmatrix} = \begin{bmatrix} \text{discounted} \\ \text{proportional} \\ \text{costs at} \\ \text{Rs. } 1{,}720/\text{ton} \end{bmatrix} + \begin{bmatrix} \text{discounted} \\ \text{investment} \\ \text{costs; see} \\ \text{equations} \\ (2.5) \text{ and} \\ (3.1) \end{bmatrix}$$

$$= \left[1{,}720 \int_{t=0}^{\infty} tD e^{-rt} dt \right] + \left[\frac{197 x^{0.77}}{1 - e^{-rx}} \right] \quad . \quad . \quad (3.2)$$

With a discount rate $r = 0.10/\text{year}$ and $D = 0.030$ million tons/year, the integral in (3.2) may be evaluated numerically. The expression is to be interpreted as the total number of discounted tons demanded over the indefinite future:

$$\int_{t=0}^{\infty} tD e^{-rt} dt = \frac{D}{r^2} = \frac{0.030}{(0.10)^2} = 3.0 \text{ million tons}$$

Dividing all terms in (3.2) by this integral (a constant factor), the discounted costs may be expressed in more familiar terms as the equivalent number of Rs./ton of aluminium demand:

$$\begin{matrix} \text{Total discounted costs} \\ \text{per ton of aluminium} \\ \text{demand over the} \\ \text{indefinite future} \\ (\text{Rs./ton}) \end{matrix} = 1{,}720 + \left[\frac{197}{3.0} \right] \left[\frac{x^{0.77}}{1 - e^{-rx}} \right] \quad . \quad (3.3)$$

In Figure 3.2, there is a plot of the cost function (3.3). Note that the minimum level of costs is Rs. 2,300/ton, and that this is achieved with a plant size corresponding to five years' worth of growth in demand, i.e. 150 thousand tons/year. With the cycle time reduced to three years (a 90 thousand ton plant), there would be a moderate but not a serious increase in costs. If, however, the Sub-group's 30 thousand ton plant size recommendation were adopted, Figure 3.2 suggests that the cost of aluminium would increase by almost Rs. 150/ton over the minimum achievable level.

For comparative purposes, Figure 3.2 also contains a horizontal line corresponding to an import price of Rs. 2,350/ton. (This c.i.f. price is equivalent to us $0.225 per pound at the official exchange rate of Rs. 4.75 per us $.) According to these calculations, India's

domestic production costs need not exceed the import price—
provided that the scale of production is at or near the optimal plant
size.[1] If foreign exchange is evaluated at the official exchange rate,
note that the minimum economic size unit would be a 60 thousand
ton plant, equivalent to two years' worth of growth.

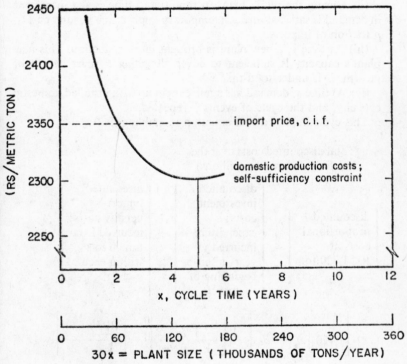

Figure 3.2.—Aluminium Plant Size and Unit Costs

Optimal plant size—time-phased imports

Figure 3.2 indicates that imports of aluminium will be more expensive
than domestic production with the optimal plant size. Nevertheless,
if imports are appropriately time-phased within the plant construction cycle, it turns out that a *combination* of imports and domestic
production can be less expensive than exclusive reliance upon either
of these alternatives. The import comparison will be evaluated at a

[1] Perhaps one further proviso should be noted—the suspension of Murphy's
law: 'If anything can go wrong, it will.'

series of alternative exchange rates, with shadow prices ranging from a zero to an infinite premium above the official rate.

The idealized sequence of events within a construction cycle is as follows:

(i) At time 0, demand has just caught up with installed domestic capacity. Demand keeps growing at a constant arithmetic rate, D.

(ii) During the phase between time 0 and time y, the increment in demand is satisfied through temporary imports at a penalty cost of p Rs./ton of imports.

(iii) At time y, a new plant is brought into production. This new plant's capacity is sufficient to cover altogether x years' worth of growth. It is understood that $x \geqslant y$.

(iv) At time x, demand has again caught up with installed domestic capacity, and the cycle of events is repeated.

This cycle implies a cost equation resembling (3.2):

$$
\begin{bmatrix} \text{Total discounted costs over the} \\ \text{indefinite future (Rs. millions)} \end{bmatrix} =
$$

$$
\begin{bmatrix} \text{discounted} \\ \text{proportional} \\ \text{costs at} \\ \text{Rs. 1,720/ton} \end{bmatrix} + \begin{bmatrix} \text{discounted} \\ \text{investment} \\ \text{costs;} \\ \text{expenditure} \\ \text{incurred } y \\ \text{years after} \\ \text{beginning of} \\ \text{each cycle} \end{bmatrix} + \begin{bmatrix} \text{discounted} \\ \text{import} \\ \text{penalty costs;} \\ \text{incurred from} \\ \text{time 0 to } y \\ \text{within each} \\ \text{cycle} \end{bmatrix}
$$

$$
= \left[1{,}720 \int_{t=0}^{\infty} tDe^{-rt}\,dt \right] + \left[\frac{e^{-ry}197x^{0\cdot77}}{1 - e^{-rx}} \right] + \left[\frac{p\int_{t=0}^{y} tDe^{-rt}\,dt}{1 - e^{-rx}} \right] \quad (3.4)
$$

In comparing equation (3.4) with the analogous one (3.2), note two effects resulting from the difference in import policies: (1) Since the temporary imports make it possible to defer the construction of initially underutilized domestic capacity, the discounted value of investment costs is now reduced through multiplication by the factor of e^{-ry}. (2) The delivered price for the temporary imports is Rs. 2,350/ton, but these expenditures make it possible to save Rs. 1,720 in domestic operating costs. That is, if the evaluation is conducted at the official exchange rate of Rs. 4·75 per US \$, the import penalty $p = 2{,}350 - 1{,}720 = $ Rs. 630/ton.[1]

[1] With a 50% premium on foreign exchange, the import cost penalty $p = 1\cdot5$ (2,350) − 1,720 = Rs. 1,805/ton. With a foreign exchange premium entering

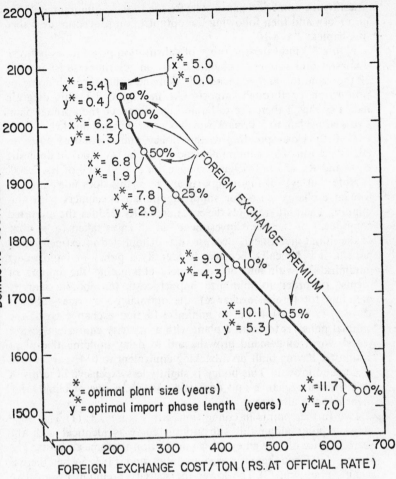

Figure 3.3.—Domestic and Foreign Exchange Cost Alternatives for Supplying Aluminium

In (3.4), the total costs depend upon two decision variables: x, the cycle time, and y, the interval over which the growth in demand is temporarily satisfied by imports. Figure 3.3 was derived through

into the cost equation (3.4), allowance must also be made for the direct import content of the capital equipment used in the production of aluminium (here taken at 40% of the initial investment). Our calculations ignore, however, the indirect effects of a foreign exchange premium upon the operating costs for such inputs as electricity, bauxite, etc.

inserting the numerical parameters for the Indian aluminium industry into (3.4), and then following the optimization procedure described in Chapters 2 and 10.

Figure 3.3 indicates the range of substitution possibilities between domestic and foreign exchange costs—at all times satisfying the 30 thousand ton annual increase in demand either through domestic production or through imports. As in Figure 3.2, this diagram indicates that if there are to be no ingot imports, the optimal plant size is equivalent to $5 \cdot 0$ years' worth of growth in demand ($x^* = 5 \cdot 0$; $y^* = 0 \cdot 0$). Corresponding to this policy, the discounted costs incurred per ton of aluminium demand would be Rs. 2,067 in domestic costs and Rs. 233 in foreign exchange, an overall total of Rs. 2,300.

Note that even if ingot imports are zero, this does not eliminate foreign exchange costs for supplying Indian consumers with aluminium. There still remains the cost item of Rs. 233 for the imported component of the plant investment—in all cases taken to be 40% of the initial investment. Because of this imported investment component, it is logically incorrect to identify a policy of import cost minimization with one of completely eliminating the import of ingots. In order to minimize import costs (an infinite scarcity premium for foreign exchange), the optimal policy is as follows: $x^* = 5 \cdot 4$; $y^* = 0 \cdot 4$. I.e. to minimize foreign exchange costs, the optimal policy is to build a plant with a capacity equivalent to $5 \cdot 4$ years' worth of demand growth, and to delay building this plant until after having built up a backlog equivalent to $0 \cdot 4$ years' worth of demand growth. This policy is slightly less expensive in terms of *both* foreign exchange and domestic costs than one of eliminating ingot imports altogether.

Two further points in connection with Figure 3.3: (1) The slope at each point along this substitution curve is identical with the scarcity price of foreign exchange in relation to domestic costs. The slope is $1 \cdot 0$ when there is a zero premium, and it is $1 \cdot 5$ when there is a 50% premium. (2) The lower the scarcity premium assigned to foreign exchange, the larger it pays to build a plant. The possibility of temporary time-phased imports only serves to reinforce the case in favour of large individual aluminium plants. Chapter 10 proves that this proposition about imports and optimal plant size is generally valid—independent of the particular numerical values assigned to the discount rate and the economies-of-scale parameter.

REFERENCES

Perspective Planning Division, *Notes on Perspective of Development, India: 1960–61 to 1975–76*, Planning Commission, New Delhi, 1964.

Reimers, J. H., 'Pre-Investment Data on the Aluminium Industry,' Centre for Industrial Development, United Nations, New York, 1963, (provisional report).

Subgroup for Aluminium, Magnesium and Silicon of the Planning Group for Non-Ferrous Metals Industry, *The Aluminium Industry*, New Delhi, 1964.

Tariff Commission, *Report on the Continuance of Protection to the Aluminium Industry*, 1960.

CHAPTER 4

CALCULATIONS FOR MULTIPLE PRODUCING AREAS

ALAN S. MANNE

Introduction

If the cost of transporting a finished product is sufficiently low relative to that of manufacturing the item, optimal plant sizes may be calculated as though all of India were served by a single producing area. In the immediately preceding chapter, this simplification was taken to be appropriate for the aluminium industry. For the three other sectors analysed in this volume (caustic soda, cement, and nitrogenous fertilizers), the cost of transporting the finished product is not negligible, and it would be misleading to proceed as though the entire nation were a single producing area. Instead, within these industries, it might well be desirable to build a large number of small plants—each located close to a different market area. The smaller plants would be unable to take advantage of economies-of-scale in manufacturing, but would be able to serve their local markets at low transport costs.[1]

This chapter describes a model of plant size, location and time-phasing for industries with multiple producing areas—each located in the vicinity of a separate market where demands are expected to grow over time.[2] The computing procedure is an approximate one, and is not guaranteed to produce an optimal solution to the stated problem. In Part III of this volume, numerical experiments are presented in order to check upon the accuracy of approximation. These experiments suggest that our plant size recommendations, although not rigorously optimal, are sufficiently reliable to deserve consideration by Indian policymakers.

---

[1] The mirror image of this case would be one in which the sources of raw material (e.g. timber, sugar cane, or raw milk) were geographically dispersed, and in which there were economies-of-scale in processing the raw material at a small number of points (e.g. lumber mills, sugar refineries, or creameries). Goran Bergendahl, in an unpublished paper dated 1964, has applied this type of mathematical programming model to a Swedish cheese producing area.

[2] Traditional location theory has dealt with multiple producing areas, but with costs and market demands during a single period of time. Computational procedures for this static case are discussed in Kuehn and Hamburger (1963), Vietorisz and Manne (1963), Cooper (1964), and Manne (1964).

Calculations for single-phase cycles

From the model of a single producing area with time-phased imports, we have already observed that the question of *when* to build interacts with the question of where and how large a plant. Time-phasing considerations may alter both the optimal size of plant and the market area to be served. By proper phasing of the construction programmes for different producing areas, it is often possible to achieve significant cost savings.

The time-phasing problem for multiple producing areas may be illustrated with an example based upon two such points—each located in the vicinity of a separate market area. It will be assumed that these areas do not import the product from the outside world, but that each can import from the other one's producing area at a constant penalty cost per unit shipped. Taking the two regions together, it is required that the installed capacity must always be at least as large as the combined demand.

Our calculations are based upon the assumption of a constant cycle time between the successive plants built within each producing region In Chapter 2, it was noted that a constant cycle time is optimal for the case of a *single* producing area with demands growing arithmetically over time, with a constant construction cost function, a constant import penalty cost function, a constant discount rate, an infinite plant life, and an infinite time horizon. Constant cycle time policies are not necessarily optimal when there are multiple producing areas.

Now define D_j as the annual arithmetic rate at which demands are growing within market area j. In order to match this demand over the long run, each plant built to serve region j will have to be of size xD_j. E.g. suppose that the cycle time $x = 3$ years, that $D_1 = 10$, and $D_2 = 5$ thousand tons/year annual increase in demand. The plant sizes built in the two regions, xD_j, would therefore be 30 and 15 thousand tons/year respectively. The cycle time x and the demand rates D_j determine the plant size built in each region, but do not indicate *when* each plant is to be built. This brings us to the problem of time-phasing.

Suppose that the analysis is being conducted at a date sufficiently early so that a plant can be brought on stream in either location at or after time zero.[1] For analytical convenience, it is assumed that there is no excess capacity available in either region at time zero. With this initial condition (a point of regeneration), we may confine the analysis to stationary cycles repeated over an infinite horizon.

[1] For our studies, time zero was taken to be April 1, 1966, the first day of India's Fourth Five Year Plan.

One timing possibility is shown on Figure 4.1, a diagram of what will hereafter be termed 'single-phase' cycles. At time zero, a 30 thousand ton plant is built in the first area, and a 15 thousand ton plant in the second. Excess capacities immediately jump up to 30 and 15 at time zero. They drift down gradually to 20 and 10 at time 1; to 10 and 5 at time 2; and to zero in both areas at time 3. The second cycle begins at time 3 with the simultaneous construction of new plants in both areas. The third cycle begins at time 6, and so on in-

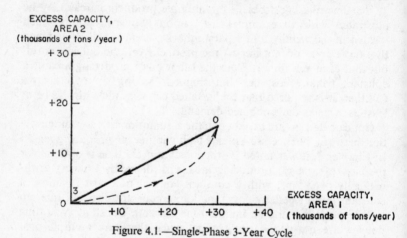

Figure 4.1.—Single-Phase 3-Year Cycle

definitely. Note that these single-phase cycles create a large amount of excess capacity in both areas simultaneously, but that they make it possible to eliminate all transport between the two. With a constant exponent function to represent construction costs for a single plant of size xD_j, the total costs over an infinite horizon would resemble the earlier equation (2.5). By similar reasoning:

Present value of future
costs discounted back to $= \dfrac{k \cdot (xD_1)^a + k \cdot (xD_2)^a}{1 - e^{-rx}}$
a point of regeneration;
single-phase cycles

$$C_1(x) = \frac{k(D_1^a + D_2^a)x^a}{1 - e^{-rx}} \qquad \cdot \quad \cdot \quad \cdot \quad (4.1)$$

Even though five numerical parameters (k, D_1, D_2, a and r) enter into equation (4.1), note that x^*, the optimal value of the cycle time, depends only upon a and r. The cross-plot of Figure 2.4 is still applicable for determining x^*.

Calculations for two-phase cycles

An altogether different possibility is shown in Figure 4.2, a diagram of 'two-phase cycles'. Now the second area's plant is delayed as long as possible, and so there is less excess capacity in the system. On the other hand, this pattern has the drawback that transport costs are incurred in order to make up for the second area's deficit during the first phase of the cycle.

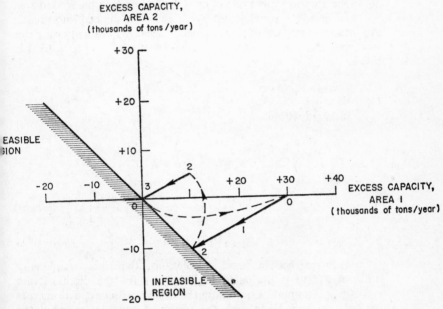

Figure 4.2.—Two-Phase 3-Year Cycle

The idealized sequence of events is this: At time zero, a 30 thousand ton plant is built in the first area, and none in the second. Shipments are made from the first to the second area in gradually increasing amounts. At time 2, it becomes necessary to build the second plant. Between time 2 and 3 (the second phase of the cycle), there are small amounts of excess capacity in both areas, and no transport is required in either direction. At time 3, the excess capacity drops to zero in both locations, a 30 thousand ton plant is constructed in the first area, and the first phase of the second cycle begins.

The duration of the first phase of each cycle will be denoted by the symbol y. It is during this phase that we defer the construction of the second plant and incur transport costs from the first to the second area. In order for the plant in region 2 to be delayed as long as possible and yet guarantee that the excess capacity vector remains within the feasible region of Figure 4.2, the following restriction[1] must be imposed upon y:

$$y = xD_1/(D_1 + D_2) \quad . \quad . \quad . \quad . \quad (4.2)$$

The total transport costs incurred during the first phase depend upon the duration y, the rate of growth of demand in the second area D_2, and upon the penalty cost p_2 for each ton shipped into area 2. An interregional flow of size tD_2 occurs exactly t years after a point of regeneration, and is discounted by a factor of e^{-rt} back to that point:

$$\therefore \text{ Present value of transport costs incurred within a cycle} = \int_{t=0}^{y} p_2 (tD_2)e^{-rt}dt$$

$$= p_2D_2 \int_{t=0}^{y} t\, e^{-rt}dt$$

$$= p_2D_2 \left[\frac{1 - e^{-ry}}{r^2} - \frac{y\, e^{-ry}}{r} \right]$$

$$= p_2D_2 \left[F(r, y) \right] \quad . \quad . \quad . \quad . \quad (4.3)$$

For convenience in hand calculations, the transport penalty function $F(r, y)$ is evaluated in Table 4.1 for the discount rate $r = 10\%$ per annum. Combining the discounted construction costs for both regions along with the transport penalties accumulated during each two-phase cycle, the present value of all costs incurred over an infinite horizon is:

$$C_2(x, y) = \frac{k(xD_1)^a + e^{-ry} k(xD_2)^a + p_2D_2F(r, y)}{1 - e^{-rx}} \quad (4.4)$$

Holding the cycle time x constant, note that expression (4.4) differs

[1] Another form of two-phase policy would consist of choosing x and y subject to a less restrictive constraint than (4.2), namely:

$$y \leqslant x\, D_1/(D_1 + D_2) \quad . \quad . \quad . \quad . \quad (4.2a)$$

With the parameter values encountered in our Indian case studies, we have found that it would not reduce costs if (4.2) were replaced by the less restrictive condition (4.2a).

in only two terms from the corresponding expression (4.1) for single-phase cycles. The difference between the two cost expressions is as follows:

$$C_2(x, y) - C_1(x) = \frac{(e^{-ry} - 1) k(xD_2)^a + p_2 D_2 F(r, y)}{1 - e^{-rx}} \quad (4.5)$$

TABLE 4.1*

Transport Penalty Function, $F(r, y) = \int_{t=0}^{y} t\, e^{-rt} dt$

$$r = 0 \cdot 100$$

y	0·000	0·100	0·200	0·300	0·400
0·500	0·120	0·172	0·233	0·303	0·381
1·000	0·467	0·562	0·664	0·775	0·893
1·500	1·018	1·151	1·291	1·438	1·591
2·000	1·752	1·919	2·092	2·272	2·458
2·500	2·649	2·847	3·050	3·259	3·474
3·000	3·693	3·918	4·148	4·383	4·622
3·500	4·867	5·116	5·369	5·627	5·889
4·000	6·155	6·425	6·699	6·977	7·258
4·500	7·543	7·832	8·124	8·420	8·718
5·000	9·020	9·325	9·632	9·943	10·256
5·500	10·572	10·891	11·212	11·536	11·861
6·000	12·190	12·520	12·853	13·187	13·524
6·500	13·862	14·202	14·544	14·888	15·233
7·000	15·580	15·928	16·278	16·629	16·982
7·500	17·335	17·690	18·046	18·403	18·761
8·000	19·120	19·480	19·841	20·202	20·565
8·500	20·928	21·291	21·656	22·020	22·386
9·000	22·751	23·117	23·484	23·851	24·218
9·500	24·585	24·953	25·320	25·688	26·056
10·000	26·424	26·791	27·159	27·527	27·895

Examples:

$$F (0 \cdot 100, 0 \cdot 500) = 0 \cdot 120$$
$$F (0 \cdot 100, 0 \cdot 600) = 0 \cdot 172$$
$$F (0 \cdot 100, 0 \cdot 900) = 0 \cdot 381$$

* Grateful acknowledgment is made to the Physics Department, University of Delhi, for permission to use its IBM 1620 computer in constructing this table.

Since the denominator of (4.5) is positive, the sign of this expression—hence the relative advantage of single- versus two-phase cycles—depends upon the magnitudes of the two terms in the numerator. The leftmost term is negative, and the rightmost is

E

positive. Holding all other parameters constant, the lower the unit transport penalty costs p_2, the more advantageous will be the two-phase cycle of plant construction.

The reader should take note of several restrictions inherent in the two-phase cycle form. Since the time interval between successive plants is assumed identical from one area to the other and since the demands are growing at different rates, it will generally be impossible to standardize the plant sizes between areas. In order to take advantage of the economies of standardization, it may be necessary to consider time sequences with much more complex periodicities than can be evaluated by hand.

Another restriction inherent in the two-phase policy is that the cycle length be uniform among all producing areas. Part III of this volume describes a heuristic computer programme (SLOT) for size, location and time-phasing problems. In SLOT, we continue to suppose that plants are to be built at constant intervals of time in each individual producing area. However, this programme removes the restriction that the cycle length be uniform among all areas.

Optimal length of two-phase cycles

Given the two-phase model described in equation (4.4), one can calculate an optimal cycle length. Just as in the case of the single producing region with unlimited temporary imports, the problem of numerical optimization may be reduced to one involving the single decision variable x rather than the two variables x and y. In the former case, y is related to x through equation (2.9)—in the present case, through equation (4.2).

Typical results of this optimization procedure are shown on Figure 4.3. The parameters a, r, k, D_1 and D_2 are all held constant, and the import penalty parameter p_2 is set at three alternative values: 0, 0·06 and 0·12.[1] Shown in solid lines are the three cost functions $C_2(x, y)$, one for each value of p_2. Shown in dotted lines for comparative purposes is the single-phase cost function $C_1(x)$.

On Figure 4.3, note that the optimal cycle length is greater for two-phase than that for single-phase cycles. Moreover, the lower the import penalties, the longer becomes the optimal cycle time, and the larger the optimal size of each plant constructed. This result closely resembles that proved for the case of the single producing region with

---

[1] If a sufficiently high value is assigned to p_2, the optimal two-phase costs will exceed those for single-phase cycles. Figure 4.3 does not illustrate this possibility. N.B. With the less restrictive constraint (4.2a) in place of (4.2), the costs of two-phase could never exceed those of single-phase cycles.

unlimited imports. Similar results—a negative relationship between the optimal plant size and the import penalty costs—have been observed in each case that the two-phase model has been evaluated numerically.

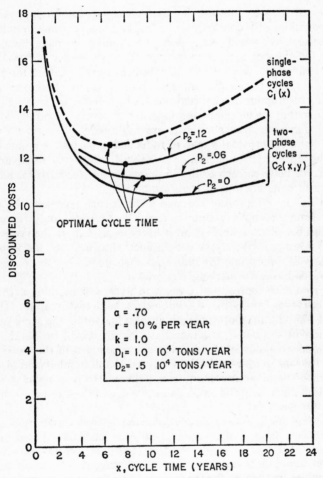

Figure 4.3.—Discounted Cost Functions; Single- and Two-Phase Cycles

On the basis of calculations of this type, we have concluded that it is safe to regard the optimal single-phase cycle length as a *lower* bound for two-phase cycles. Frequently, in order to reduce the volume of hand calculations, we did not explicitly optimize the two-phase cycle length, but instead evaluated costs as though the cycle length and plant size were fixed at this lower bound.

Producing and consuming areas

In each industry studied, it has been convenient to suppose that production and consumption takes place at a finite number of predetermined points—not along a continuum in space. Because of the difficulty of making long-range forecasts in any greater detail, the general practice has been to consider an entire state as the unit of analysis, and to calculate transport costs as though both production and consumption are concentrated at a single 'representative point' within that state—either the largest or the most centrally located city. *Intra*state transport costs are neglected.[1]

Figure 4.4 provides a map of India and indicates the points taken to be representative of each state. Table 4.2 shows the minimum rail distance between each of the 16 points, and is the basis for all subsequent computations of transport costs.[2]

This simplification of the map of India (one representative point per state and no intrastate transport) is intended only for use in industries where a single plant is likely to serve more than one state. It is not a general-purpose geographical classification, and would be clearly inappropriate for industries that are known to be oriented towards intrastate markets, e.g. bricks.

From each representative point to its closest neighbour, the distance ranges from 310 to 690 kilometres. With two exceptions (Patna and Bhopal), the closest neighbour also lies within the same general region of the country: either East, North, West, or South. This regional grouping of states fits in conveniently with the location of the four major cities of India: Calcutta, Delhi, Bombay and Madras. Each of these metropolitan areas is known to be a point of large-scale demand for products such as caustic soda and cement—though not for fertilizers.

Using this geographical classification of states and regions, the hand calculations of optimal plant sizes have been based on the assumption that a plant is built to serve one of three alternative

---

[1] In one state, we do allow for intrastate transport. This exception is Uttar Pradesh, India's most populous state. This is treated as though it contained two representative points—one in the east at Kanpur and one in the west at Delhi.

[2] Upon request, the author will supply a report listing rail rates between each of the 16 representative points. 1964 rates are provided for each of the following commodities: caustic soda, cement, coal, ammonia, naphtha, ammonium sulphate, and urea.

market areas: (1) a state, (2) a region, or (3) the entire nation. The lower the transport costs in relation to economies-of-scale in manufacturing, the more favourable will cases (2) or (3) become. Both

Figure 4.4.—Location of Representative Points

cases (2) and (3) are bound to arouse political opposition from individual states—each of which is seeking to promote its own industrial growth.

TABLE 4.2

Rail distance between representative points (thousands of kilometres)

		EAST				NORTH					WEST			SOUTH			
		Assam	Bihar	Orissa	West Bengal	Jammu & Kashmir	Punjab	Rajasthan	Uttar Pradesh	Delhi	Gujarat	Madhya Pradesh	Maharashtra	Andhra Pradesh	Kerala	Mysore	Madras
		Gauhati	Patna	Cuttack	Calcutta	Srinagar*	Jullundur	Jaipur	Kanpur	Delhi	Ahmadabad	Bhopal	Bombay	Hyderabad	Cochin	Bangalore	Madras
EAST	Gauhati	—	0·61	1·44	1·03	1·47	1·36	1·59	1·09	1·53	2·21	1·58	2·99	2·42	3·38	3·04	2·68
	Patna	0·61†	—	0·94	0·53	1·21	1·09	0·97	0·47	0·91	1·59	0·96	1·63	1·78	2·89	2·48	2·19
	Cuttack	1·44	0·94	—	0·41†	2·28	2·16	1·91	1·42	1·85	2·54	1·92	1·97	1·18	1·95	1·61	1·25
	Calcutta	1·03	0·53	0·41†	—	1·87	1·75	1·50	1·01	1·44	2·13	1·51	1·97	1·59	2·36	2·01	1·66
NORTH	Srinagar*	1·47	1·21	2·28	1·87	—	0·12†	0·79	0·92	0·48	1·42	1·19	1·87	2·16	3·37	2·85	2·67
	Jullundur	1·36	1·09	2·16	1·75	0·12	—	0·67	0·80	0·37†	1·30	1·07	1·75	2·04	3·25	2·74	2·55
	Jaipur	1·59	0·97	1·91	1·50	0·79	0·67	—	0·50	0·31†	0·63	0·57	1·12	1·55	2·86	2·27	2·23
	Kanpur	1·09	0·47†	1·42	1·01	0·92	0·80	0·50	—	0·43	1·12	0·55†	1·35	1·49	2·69	2·18	1·99
	Delhi	1·53	0·91	1·85	1·44	0·48	0·37†	0·031†	0·43†	—	0·93	0·70	1·38	1·68	2·89	2·38	2·19
WEST	Ahmadabad	2·21	1·59	2·54	2·13	1·42	1·30	0·63	1·12	0·93	—	0·58	0·49†	1·28	2·24	1·61	1·77
	Bhopal	1·58	0·96	1·92	1·51	1·19	1·07	0·57	0·55	0·70	0·58	—	0·84	0·97	2·29	1·67	1·48
	Bombay	2·99	1·63	1·97	1·97	1·87	1·75	1·12	1·35	1·38	0·49†	0·84	—	0·79	1·74	1·11	1·28
SOUTH	Hyderabad	2·42	1·78	1·18	1·59	2·16	2·04	1·55	1·49	1·68	1·28	0·97	0·79	—	1·32	0·69	0·79
	Cochin	3·38	2·89	1·95	2·36	3·37	3·25	2·86	2·69	2·89	2·24	2·29	1·74	1·32	—	0·62	0·70
	Bangalore	3·04	2·48	1·61	2·01	2·85	2·74	2·27	2·18	2·38	1·61	1·67	1·11	0·69†	0·62†	—	0·36†
	Madras	2·68	2·19	1·25	1·66	2·67	2·55	2·23	1·99	2·19	1·77	1·48	1·28	0·79	0·70	0·36†	—

* Rail distance is shown only to Pathankot. From Pathankot to Srinagar, the road distance is an additional 400 kilometres.
† Closest neighbouring point to city specified in column heading.

REFERENCES

Cooper, L., 'Heuristic Methods for Location–Allocation Problems', *SIAM Review*, January 1964.

Kuehn, A. A., and M. J. Hamburger, 'A Heuristic Program for Locating Warehouses', *Management Science*, July 1963.

Manne, A. S., 'Plant Location under Economies-of-Scale—Decentralization and Computation', *Management Science*, November 1964.

Vietorisz, T., and A. S. Manne, 'Chemical Processes, Plant Location, and Economies of Scale', Ch. 6 in A. S. Manne and H. M. Markowitz (eds.), *Studies in Process Analysis*, John Wiley & Sons, New York, 1963.

CHAPTER 5

THE CAUSTIC SODA INDUSTRY

ALAN S. MANNE[1]

Summary

This analysis of the caustic soda industry applies both the single- and the two-phase models for multiple areas. The chapter begins by outlining the basic data inputs: demand forecasts, investment costs, raw material costs, byproduct utilization, and transport costs. Each of these elements required a combination of both judgment and objective facts. On the basis of the data that appeared most reasonable, the model yields the following policy recommendations:

(1) An uncoordinated, state-by-state approach to planning is distinctly uneconomical in the caustic soda industry.

(2) One recommended pattern of plant size and location emerges if we assume that the principal raw material costs—electricity and salt —are roughly the same throughout the country. In this instance, the balance between transport costs and economies-of-scale in manufacturing is such that it is desirable to set up plants to serve five years' worth of growth in each of the major regions of the country—East, North, West and South. In order to take full advantage of these regional plants, their dates of construction should be staggered, and temporary interregional shipments should be planned in order to offset temporary deficits in regional capacity.

(3) An altogether different pattern emerges if it is believed that there is one region—perhaps the South or the East—which enjoys a commanding advantage in electricity and/or salt costs. It would then be optimal to concentrate the entire new national capacity in that single region, and to build large plants there at two-year intervals.

(4) Regardless of which assumption is made with respect to electricity and salt costs, the model recommends capacity increments that are much larger than the current practice in India. The recommended sizes for new plants range from approximately 50 thousand tons/year upwards. This contrasts with the fact that on January 1, 1964, India had 19 caustic soda plants (most of them built in several

---

[1] The author is indebted to Pitambar Pant and K. K. Sarin for data and for helpful comments on this study.

increments), averaging 10 thousand tons/year in total size. (See Appendix A.) To date, the largest capacity increment has been 28 thousand tons (Dhrangadhra Chemical Works in Madras State).

(5) The model is not explicitly concerned with standardization of plant sizes, but the results happen to be compatible with standardization. Depending upon one's views with respect to regional uniformity of salt and power costs, the recommended sizes would be either: (*a*) 50 and 150, or (*b*) 100 thousand tons/year.

Demand forecasts

Both exports and imports are excluded from this industry study. Table 5.1 contains the forecasts of domestic demand used here. They are derived through a material balance for each state of India. For each end use of caustic soda, a consumption target is set for the terminal years of the Third and Fourth Plan periods, 1965–66 and 1970–71 respectively. On the basis of consumption norms, the end uses are translated into requirements for caustic soda. E.g. in Table 5.1, the Andhra Pradesh requirements for caustic soda by paper and paperboard are shown as 9·90 thousand tons for 1970–71. The figure is derived through estimating that state's target for paper and paperboard at 99 thousand tons/year and applying a consumption norm of 0·10 ton/ton.

The demand forecast implies virtually a doubling of total consumption and production over the Fourth Plan period: from 324 to 617 thousand tons/year. From 1965–66 onwards, it is expected that India will no longer be an importer of caustic soda.

If demand grows during the Fourth Plan period at the rates estimated in Table 5.1, the average annual increments on a state-by-state basis are as shown in Table 5.2. This table also indicates the plant sizes that would be necessary in order for a single unit to serve *five* years' worth of average growth in each of the three alternative market areas: (1) a state, (2) a region, or (3) the entire nation. In subsequent calculations, we explore the costs of using both a two-year as well as a five-year time interval between the construction of plants designed to serve a given market area.

In order to apply any of the models described in the previous chapter, it is necessary to select a date for time zero. This is taken to be April 1, 1966. From that date onwards, it is supposed that the plant size, location, and time-phasing may be selected with complete freedom from the constraints imposed by construction lags. For convenience in computation, it is supposed that there is no excess capacity at time zero, and that the individual plant capacities in

TABLE 5.1

Caustic soda demand projections (thousand tons/year, 100% caustic soda)

Consuming product	Paper and paperboard	Newsprint	Viscose rayon yarn and staple fibre	Soap	Aluminium	Petroleum refining	Vanaspati	Cresols and phenol	Dyestuffs	Synthetic detergents	Textiles	Others including small-scale	Total demands
Consumption norm (ton/ton)	0·10	0·05	1·00	0·10	0·20	0·0006	0·01	0·34	0·70	0·34	—	—	—
Andhra Pradesh	5·80			0·29		0·60	0·20				0·28		7·17
Assam						0·80							0·80
Bihar	8·10			0·18		1·20	0·14				0·02		9·64
Gujarat	5·60		3·00	0·06		1·20	0·33		2·80		10·70		23·69
Jammu & Kashmir													
Kerala	1·00		5·50	2·02	3·20	1·50	0·05				0·12		13·39
Madhya Pradesh	7·80	3·70	22·00	0·27			0·11	1·43			3·14		38·45
Madras	4·50		8·00	0·99	2·00		0·17				1·06		16·72
Maharashtra	11·10		32·00	11·56	4·00	3·70	1·32	0·51	3·70	7·00	13·45		88·34
Mysore	7·60			0·41			0·14				0·55		8·70
Orissa	10·10				4·00			0·14			0·28		14·52
Punjab	5·00			0·26			0·13		0·20		0·52		6·11
Rajasthan	0·80		4·00								0·43		5·23
Uttar Pradesh	7·20		4·00	1·61	12·00		0·87				2·78		28·46
West Bengal	14·10		4·00	7·39	1·40		0·82				2·15		29·86
Union Territories				0·48			0·42		0·40		1·62		2·92
Total	88·70	3·70	82·50	25·52	26·60	9·00	4·70	2·08	7·10	7·00	37·10	30·00	324·00

1965–66

TABLE 5.1

Caustic soda demand projections (continued) (thousands tons/year, 100% caustic soda)

Consuming product	Paper and paperboard	Newsprint	Viscose rayon yarn and staple fibre	Soap	Aluminium	Petroleum refining	Vanaspati	Cresols and phenol	Dyestuffs	Synthetic detergents	Textiles	Others including small-scale	Total demands
Andhra Pradesh	9·90			0·80		0·70	0·34				0·34		12·08
Assam	8·40					1·00							9·40
Bihar	11·10			0·49		1·80	0·23			5·00	0·02		18·64
Gujarat	5·60		6·20	0·16		1·80	0·57		4·20	5·00	12·82		36·35
Jammu & Kashmir		1·50											1·50
Kerala	7·00		11·40	5·54	4·00	2·10	0·09				0·14		30·27
Madhya Pradesh	10·80	3·70	45·50	0·74	10·00		0·19	1·84			3·77		76·54
Madras	4·60		16·60	2·72	4·00	2·00	0·29	0·85			1·27		32·33
Maharashtra	19·60	3·00	66·20	31·70	10·00	3·70	2·24		5·60	7·00	16·10		165·14
Mysore	10·30			1·13	12·0		0·25				0·66		24·34
Orissa	13·10				4·00			2·11			0·34		19·55
Punjab	8·00	3·00		0·71			0·22		0·35		0·62		12·90
Rajasthan	0·80		8·30			1·50					0·52		11·12
Uttar Pradesh	15·50	1·50	8·30	4·42	20·00		1·48				3·34		54·54
West Bengal	14·10		8·30	20·27	4·00	1·20	1·39				2·58		51·84
Union Territories				1·32			0·71		0·49		1·94		4·46
Total	138·80	12·70	170·80	70·00	68·00	15·80	8·00	4·80	10·64	17·00	44·46	56·00	617·00

(1970–71)

Source: Unpublished estimates by K. K. Sarin, Assistant Chief, Perspective Planning Division, Planning Commission.

TABLE 5.2

Alternative plant sizes, five-year cycles
(thousand tons/year, 100% caustic soda)

Region	State	Case 1 State market areas	Case 2 Regional market areas	Case 3 National market area	Annual increase in statewide demand‡
East	Assam	9·5			1·9
	Bihar	10·0			2·0
	Orissa	5·5			1·1
	West Bengal*	24·0	49·0		4·8
North	Punjab, J. & K.	9·0			1·8
	Rajasthan	6·5			1·3
	U.P.—east†	17·0			3·4
	Delhi Territory, U.P.—west*†	13·0	45·5		2·6
West	Gujarat	14·0			2·8
	Madhya Pradesh	42·0			8·4
	Maharashtra*	84·5	140·5	293·0	16·9
South	Andhra Pradesh	5·5			1·1
	Kerala	18·5			3·7
	Mysore	17·0			3·4
	Madras*	17·0	58·0		3·4
	Total	293·0	293·0	293·0	58·6

* Regional centre.

† The demands of Uttar Pradesh are split up, with 60% allocated to U.P.—east and 40% to U.P.—west. Among the state's cities with 1961 population in excess of 100,000 persons, there is a 60–40 division of population between those that are closer to Kanpur and those closer to Delhi.

‡ In Table 5.1, there is no state-by-state breakdown of caustic soda demand by 'others'. Here this category is distributed among states in the same proportion as the caustic soda demand in all remaining categories.

existence will thereafter continue to be allocated to the same states as those served at time zero.

Investment costs

In estimating economies-of-scale in investment costs, reliance has been placed upon data published in United Nations, Economic

Commission for Latin America (1963, p. 265). These international data have been used rather than Indian sources for several reasons: (1) Plant sizes shown in the ECLA report range up to 100,000 tons/year—almost four times the size of the largest capacity increment experienced in India. (2) Among the 19 existing plants, some use the now-obsolescent chemical process, and others use carbon electrode cells. The ECLA data refer exclusively to the process being introduced in new Indian plants, the mercury cathode process. (3) Finally— and perhaps most important—there are known to be large variations in Indian investment costs depending upon the financing arrangements and the foreign currency to which the plant's equipment purchase has been tied.

The ECLA report gives estimates of Latin American investment costs (within battery limits, exclusive of utilities, administration buildings, and housing) for four alternative plant sizes.[1] Within the entire range of $16 \cdot 5$ to $100 \cdot 0$ thousand tons/year, the economies-of-scale parameter $a = 0 \cdot 77$. That is, for each increase of $1 \cdot 00\%$ in the capacity of a single *balanced* plant installation, there will be a corresponding increase of $0 \cdot 77\%$ in the total investment cost.

The largest plant size considered in the ECLA report has an annual capacity of 100 thousand tons and an investment cost of Rs. $98 \cdot 5$ million.[2] In order to extrapolate to still larger plant sizes than this, it has been assumed that the *incremental* costs will remain constant at Rs. 760/ton. This is the incremental cost at a plant size of 100 thousand tons/year. Algebraically, if we denote the cycle time by x, the annual demand increment by D, and the plant size by xD thousand tons/year, the total initial investment costs $f(xD)$ are assumed to behave in the following fashion:

xD below 100 thousand tons/year

$$f(xD) = 98 \cdot 5 \left(\frac{xD}{100}\right)^{0 \cdot 77} \text{ Rs. million}$$

xD at or above 100 thousand tons/year

$$f(xD) = 98 \cdot 5 + 0 \cdot 760 \, (xD - 100) \text{ Rs. million}$$

The ECLA report suggests a figure for maintenance at 4% on the

[1] One rough check of the ECLA figures has been made against Indian data. In Perspective Planning Division (1963), an investment coefficient of Rs. 1,500 is given for each ton of annual electrolytic caustic soda capacity in new units. At a plant size of 15 thousand tons/year, the ECLA investment estimate would be identical with this coefficient.

[2] The ECLA cost of Rs. $98 \cdot 5$ millions is for a plant with a *chlorine* capacity of 100 thousand tons, i.e. a caustic soda capacity of 111. In effect, a uniform safety factor of 10% has been added on to the Latin American investment costs.

initial capital investment. If these costs occur in perpetuity and if the annual discount rate is taken to be 10%, the present value of all future maintenance costs is equivalent to 40% on the initial investment.

To allow for future replacement, the initial investment costs are multiplied by the replacement factor ρ. (See equation (2.6) above.) With a discount rate of 10%, in order to pay for an infinite series of replacements of the original caustic soda plant at 24-year intervals, $\rho = 1 \cdot 10$. After adding the 40% maintenance factor together with the replacement factor, the investment cost function $f(xD)$ actually used in the calculations becomes:

xD below 100 thousand tons/year:

$$f(xD) = 148 \left(\frac{xD}{100}\right)^{0 \cdot 77} \text{ Rs. million} \tag{5.1}$$

xD at or above 100 thousand tons/year:

$$f(xD) = 148 + 1 \cdot 14 \, (xD - 100) \text{ Rs. million}$$

Raw material and other proportional costs

Table 5.3 contains a list of inputs and outputs per ton of caustic soda production. For short, the inputs on this list will hereafter be referred to as 'proportional costs'. In order to compare the relative economic importance of the various inputs and outputs, approximate prices are assigned to each of these items. It will be noted that an overwhelming fraction of the proportional input costs are associated with electricity and salt. (Rs. 329/Rs. 370 = 89%.)

Both salt and electricity prices differ considerably from one point of India to another. Undoubtedly, some of these cost differences are real, but others are the artificial result of promotional pricing policies followed by the electricity boards in certain states. Now if there is one region of the country in which the electricity and/or salt prices are much lower than anywhere else, and if there are no political constraints on economic efficiency, it will pay to concentrate the entire caustic soda industry there—regardless of economies-of-scale.

In order to focus upon the economies-of-scale problem, the initial comparisons will be made *as though* proportional costs are uniform throughout the country. In a second round of calculations, the comparisons will be made as though one single region of the country had an electricity-or-salt cost advantage of Rs. 70/ton of caustic soda over all other regions. (Since the electricity input is 3,500 kilowatt-hours, an interregional differential of Rs. $0 \cdot 02$/kwhr would be enough to account for a cost differential of Rs. 70/ton of caustic soda.) Today, because of hydroelectricity and a favourable coastline for salt collection, the Southern region might possess a cost advantage of Rs. 70. In the future, because of the scarcity of Southern hydro projects and because the Eastern region may be able to base its thermal electricity upon coal middlings, it is possible that the Eastern region will come to enjoy a cost advantage over all others.

TABLE 5.3

Inputs and outputs proportional to caustic soda production
(excludes investment, labour and overheads)

	Physical quantity*	Approximate price per physical unit	Value of input or output
Inputs			
Salt	1·4 ton	Rs. 60·00	Rs. 84
Mercury	0·2 kg.	33·00	7
Graphite	2·2 kg.	0·50	1
Other chemical products	2·2 us $	4·75	10
Fuel	1·8 10⁶ kg.cal.	7·00	13
Electric energy	3,500·0 kw.hr.	0·07	245
Treated water	20·0 m³	0·50	10
Total value of inputs			370
Outputs			
Caustic soda (100%)	1·00 ton	Rs. 700†	Rs. 700
Chlorine	0·90 ton	440	396
Hydrogen	0·023 ton	230‡	5
Total value of outputs			1,101

* Source: United Nations, Economic Commission for Latin America (1963, p. 265).

† Controlled price shown here; the open-market price for caustic soda might range up to Rs. 1,400/ton.

‡ Valued as fuel gas at Rs. 7.00/10⁶ kg.cal.

These future cost differences are highly debatable. The first round of calculations in this report is therefore based upon the assumption of identical proportional costs throughout all states. Now if it is assumed that (1) proportional costs are identical throughout the country, and (2) the country's total output equals the demand fixed for each point of time in the future, then it follows that the proportional manufacturing costs constitute a fixed charge, independent of the plant size, location and timing decisions. For the purpose of making such decisions, these constant elements may be omitted from the cost comparison. In the second round of calculations, where the proportional costs are no longer assumed to be identical at all points, this omission is no longer permissible.

Because of the lack of reliable data under Indian conditions, it seemed best to omit certain minor cost categories altogether: operating labour, plant overheads, and community housing. Each of these elements is believed to be subject to economies-of-scale, and these omissions tend to bias the results in favour of small plant sizes.

Byproduct utilization

According to Table 5.3, each ton of 100% caustic soda is accompanied by 0·90 tons of chlorine and 0·023 tons of hydrogen as byproducts in the mercury cathode electrolytic process. These items have a significant money value to many caustic soda producers. However, in the following calculations, the scale and location of caustic soda plants is regarded as independent of the scale and location of demand for the byproducts.[1]

The omission of the byproducts can be justified if it is assumed that their demands are 'footloose', i.e. that the using industries will gravitate towards wherever the chlorine and hydrogen are produced. The assumption of footloose demand seems quite justifiable in the case of chlorine consumption for the manufacture of PVC (polyvinyl chloride) plastic, a weight-losing process in which chlorine is a major input. On the other hand, the assumption is unlikely to hold true in the case of the paper industry's demand for chlorine. Paper manufacture is a weight-losing process where chlorine is a minor input.

In order to put this byproduct utilization problem into perspective, it is worth examining the orders-of-magnitude shown in Table 5.4. According to these projections, two points stand out clearly. For both these reasons, it seems unlikely that the chlorine demands will exert a major influence over caustic soda plant location in the near future: (1) The chemical uses of chlorine are the ones most likely to be footloose. During the Fourth Plan, it is projected that the absolute increase in these uses (88 thousand tons) will be approximately equal to the increase in non-chemical uses. (2) Even in 1970–71, it is projected that there will continue to be a substantial excess available of the byproduct chlorine over the demand. The dispersed uses (paper,

[1] Under Indian conditions, the domestic availability of byproduct chlorine tends to exceed the domestic demand. It is reasonable to suppose that the aggregate output will continue to be set by the aggregate demand for caustic soda, and will be independent of the detailed decisions with respect to plant size, location and time-phasing. Since the aggregate demand for caustic soda is regarded as a datum at any future point of time, so also will be the aggregate byproduct availability.

textile bleaching, solvents and water purification) could probably be met through the 19 dispersed plants already in existence in 1964.

Neither the tonnage nor the value of the byproduct hydrogen can be as significant in plant size and location decisions as the tonnage and value of the byproduct chlorine. The hydrogen may be used as a fuel gas, or it may be put to higher-value uses in manufacturing hydrogenated vegetable oils, or hydrochloric acid, or methanol, or ammonia. In view of economies-of-scale in chemical processes, the larger the caustic soda plant the more advantageous will become these particular uses of the hydrogen byproduct.

TABLE 5.4

Chlorine material balance projections
(thousands of tons)

	1963		1965–66		1970–71	
Chemical uses						
Ammonium chloride	4		6		12	
Stable bleaching powder	4		8		12	
Insecticides	7		15		25	
Inorganic chlorides	3		5		10	
Polyvinyl chloride plastic	2		15		50	
Organic chemicals	1		5		15	
Phosphoric acid, etc.	nil		6		20	
Misc. as hydrochloric acid and chlorine gas	5		15		19	
Sub-total		26		75		163
Non-chemical uses						
Paper, pulp and newsprint	50		75		150	
Textile bleaching	5		8		12	
Solvents and refrigeration gases	nil		2		5	
Water purification	5		10		15	
Sub-total		60		95		182
Unutilized chlorine surplus	26		60		115	
Total byproduct chlorine available	112		230		460	

Source: Unpublished estimates by K. K. Sarin.

To sum up: The larger the scale of caustic soda production at any one point, the more economical it will be to upgrade the hydrogen and chlorine byproducts for further manufacture as chemicals at that point. Offsetting this advantage of concentrated production is the disadvantage that some of the bulk users of chlorine (paper and water purification) are widely dispersed in India. These users would have no significant tendency to gravitate toward the source of

F

chlorine. On balance, the offsetting factors seem to cancel out, and to justify the viewpoint adopted here. Neither credits nor debits are attached to the location or scale of production of the chlorine and hydrogen byproducts.

Transport costs

Transport costs are estimated as though a state's entire production and consumption takes place at a single 'representative point'. *Intra*-state transport is therefore omitted from the cost comparisons.

In order to simplify calculations still further, it has been supposed that any *inter*state shipments originate from one or another of the four major metropolitan areas: Calcutta, Delhi, Bombay and Madras. This means that there are definite inefficiencies built into the model. (For example, new capacity in Rajasthan could be used only to supply itself, and could not be used for shipping caustic soda into its four neighbouring states.) With the electronic computer programme SLOT described in Part III, it would no longer make any difference whether interstate shipments were restricted to the four regional centres considered here.

In order to estimate shipping charges, it has been necessary to make some assumption with respect to the physical form in which caustic soda will move: as 50% liquid mixture with water, as 75% liquid, or as a solid that is virtually 100% concentration. (All the demand and cost calculations are worked out here in terms of equivalents to a 100% caustic soda product.) *A priori*, it would seem that the more concentrated the form in which caustic soda is shipped, the less water is being transported via rail, and the more economical the operation. It turns out, however, that the dehydration costs are also considerable.[1]

Because of the substantial cost of complete dehydration and also because the solid form precludes movement in specialized tank wagons, it was decided to compute transport costs as though all shipments took place in the form of 50% liquid. With this assumption, we have probably overstated the actual transport costs, and to this extent biased the results in favour of small dispersed units.

The transport rates shown in Table 5.5 are those applicable to rail shipments of caustic soda in wagon loads. They have been

[1] According to one firm, it costs them roughly Rs. 100 per ton of caustic soda for the equipment, fuel, labour, and steel drums needed in order to convert 50% liquid into solid form. At a shipping distance of 1,600 kilometres, the rail tariff is Rs. 52 per ton of bulk. To transport the liquid, it would therefore cost Rs. 104 per ton of 100% caustic soda. Even at this long distance, shipment in liquid form would be less expensive than paying for dehydration costs of Rs. 100 per ton.

calculated on the basis of: (a) the rail distances between representative points shown above in Table 4.2, (b) the 50% ratio of caustic soda to total bulk transported, and (c) the rail charges for transport over alternative distances, Table 5.10, Appendix B of this chapter. Appendix B also discusses some of the pros and cons involved in using the published tariffs as an approximation to the country's real costs of rail transport.

TABLE 5.5

Rail rates between representative points, wagon loads
(Rs./ton of 100% caustic soda in 50% solution)

From / To	West Bengal Calcutta	Delhi Territory, U.P.—west Delhi	Maharash-tra Bombay	Madras Madras
East Assam				
Gauhati	77·5	100·0	157·0	146·0
Bihar Patna	49·5	70·5	104·5	127·5
Orissa Cuttack	40·5	114·5	119·5	88·0
West Bengal				
Calcutta	0	96·5	119·5	106·0
North Punjab, J. & K.				
Jullundur	110·0	37·5	110·0	141·0
Rajasthan Jaipur	99·0	33·0	81·5	129·0
Uttar Pradesh–				
east Kanpur	76·0	42·5	92·5	121·0
Delhi Territory,				
U.P.—west				
Delhi	96·5	0	94·0	127·5
West Gujarat				
Ahmadabad	125·5	72·0	46·5	111·0
Madhya Pradesh				
Bhopal	99·5	59·5	66·5	98·5
Maharashtra				
Bombay	119·5	94·0	0	89·5
South Andhra Pradesh				
Hyderabad	103·0	107·0	64·0	64·0
Kerala Cochin	134·0	153·0	109·5	59·0
Mysore				
Bangalore	121·5	134·5	81·5	36·5
Madras Madras	106·0	127·5	89·5	0

Cost comparisons, single-phase cycles, uniform proportional costs

All the data inputs have now been described: state-by-state forecasts of the rate of growth of demand, the economies-of-scale relationship for plant investment costs, the transport costs, and the assumptions with respect to byproduct utilization. Overall cost comparisons are now presented in terms of present value over an infinite horizon, using a discount rate of 10% per annum.

Table 5.6 summarizes the results under the assumptions of (*a*) uniform proportional costs, and (*b*) single-phase two-year and five-year cycles. Since the proportional costs (electricity, salt, etc.) are taken to be uniform in this table, it has already been argued that these may be excluded from the comparison. By a 'single-phase' two- or five-year cycle, it is meant that a balanced plant is to be constructed every two or five years beginning with time zero.

For single-phase cycles, it is known that five-year intervals are optimal *provided*: (*a*) the successive plants are built at a single producing location to serve a fixed market area; (*b*) the discount rate $r = 10\%$ per annum; and (*c*) the economies-of-scale parameter $a = 0 \cdot 77$. (See Figure 2.4 in Chapter 2.) For comparative purposes, the effect of two-year spacing is also included in Table 5.6. This shorter interval is intended to convey some rough idea of the magnitude of loss imposed by political or ideological constraints upon the size of caustic soda plants.

In combination with the two time intervals, there are three alternative market areas considered within Table 5.6. It is supposed that successive plants within a single state are built to satisfy the growth in demand within: (1) the state, (2) the region, or (3) the entire nation. The actual physical sizes of these plants have already been indicated in Table 5.2 above.

To simplify the hand calculations, only the four regional centres are considered as possible sources of interstate shipments: Calcutta, Delhi, Bombay and Madras. In case (2), where plants are built to satisfy the regional market, each of these four points is regarded as the source of supply of its entire region. In case (3), where a single plant is built to satisfy the entire national market growth over a two- or a five-year interval, Maharashtra is regarded as the best location. Of the four alternative sources of interstate shipments, this is the point that minimizes total transport costs.

Within each of the six combinations of time interval and market areas shown in Table 5.6, there are separate entries for the plant investment component (I) and for the interstate transport (T). With this breakdown of costs, it is an easy further step to calculate the effect of, say, a uniform 25% increase in rail transport rates or a

TABLE 5.6

*Present value of costs over infinite horizon,
excluding proportional costs. Single-phase cycles. (Rs. millions)*

		Case 1 State market areas; each individual state perpetually supplies itself			Case 2 Regional market areas; regional centre perpetually supplies all states in region			Case 3 National market area; Maharashtra perpetually supplies all states		
		I	T	$I+T$	I	T	$I+T$	I	T	$I+T$
Single-phase, two-year cycles	East	313	0	313	232	29	261	0	121	121
	North	300	0	300	221	26	247	0	86	86
	West	653	0	653	525	69	594	926	69	995
	South	360	0	360	262	41	303	0	106	106
	Total	1,626	0	1,626	1,240	165	1,405	926	382	1,308
Single-phase, five-year cycles	East	291	0	291	218	29	247	0	121	121
	North	279	0	279	205	26	231	0	86	86
	West	607	0	607	494	69	563	936	69	1,005
	South	336	0	336	247	41	288	0	106	106
	Total	1,513	0	1,513	1,164	165	1,329	936	382	1,318

uniform reduction in the bulk of water shipped per ton of caustic soda.

Of the six combinations of plant size and market area, there is one that is clearly the most expensive: two-year cycles, state market areas. For this, the required plant sizes would range from 2·2 up to 33·8 thousand tons/year. (Roughly speaking, these plant increments would be of the same dimensions as those that have been used for constructing the 19 plants existing in India today.) The present value of costs for this expensive future system would amount to Rs. 1,626 millions.

Keeping the same two-year time interval but switching over to case 3, a national market area served by Maharashtra, there would be a significant reduction in the total of investment and transport costs, a drop of Rs. 318 down to Rs. 1,308 millions. In order to meet a two-year increment in national demand, the units to be constructed would be sizeable (117·2 thousand tons/year capacity for each plant). The economies-of-scale in these large plants would—at least on paper—be more than enough to pay for the increase of Rs. 382 millions in transport costs.

According to Table 5.6, there are interactions between the choice of time interval and of geographical area to be served. The time and space decisions cannot be completely isolated from each other. If plants are built to cover either a single state or a single regional market area (cases 1 and 2), the costs are minimized by using a five-year cycle time. On the other hand, in case 3 where a single plant location is employed to serve the entire national market, it is no longer optimal to employ this cycle length. The five-year plant size (293·0 thousand tons/year) is well above the range in which it is assumed that the economies-of-scale parameter a has a value of 0·77.[1]

Cost comparisons, two-phase cycles, uniform proportional costs

The preceding section dealt with the interrelated problems of plant size and location. We now take up the time-phasing problem, but still retain the assumption of uniform proportional costs at all of the potential producing locations.

For single-phase cycles, it was assumed that a producing location

---

[1] With the investment cost function (5.1), it turns out that if a single location is to serve the entire national market, a time interval of three years would be optimal. For this interval, the transport costs (T) remain unchanged at Rs. 382 millions, and the investment costs (I) are slightly reduced to Rs. 905 millions.

always keeps serving the identical market area. No advantage was taken of the possibility of building a plant in one area, temporarily delaying the investment in a plant for a second area, and temporarily incurring the cost of shipment from the first to the second area. Now, staggered time-phasing is to be analysed through the device of 'two-phase' cycles.

In order to apply the two-phase cost equation (4.4) to the caustic soda problem, several choices must be made. First a cycle length has to be selected. In order to make direct comparisons between the single- and two-phase calculations, the cycle length x is set equal to five years. This value is known to be optimal for single-phase cycles with $a = 0 \cdot 77$ and $r = 0 \cdot 10$, and is slightly shorter than optimal for the two-phase model.

After fixing the cycle length at five years, a number of geographical alternatives have to be considered. In case 2, for example, during each cycle there are four plants to be built—one to serve that cycle's demand growth in the East, the North, the West and the South. A priori, it is not obvious which of the four should be built in the first and which in the second phase of each five-year cycle. Only one of many possibilities is considered here. The first phase plant is built in the West (the area with the largest rate of increase in demand), and the second phase plants are built simultaneously in the East, North and South. For short, this sequence is labelled in Table 5.7 as 'West alternates with three other regions'.

Altogether, Table 5.7 contains the results for three sequencing patterns. Under case 1 (state market areas), plant sizes for each state are chosen so as to meet five years' worth of internal demand. Although these sizes are identical with those considered previously for the single-phase cycles, there is a substantial difference in the present value of costs, a drop from Rs. 1,513 to Rs. 1,355 or to Rs. 1,367 millions. Although the two-phase cycles require higher transport costs, these *temporary* transport costs are highly profitable. They make it possible to defer a substantial volume of investments until the second phase of each cycle.

Among all the possible combinations of size, locations, and time-phasing, the least expensive one in Tables 5.6 and 5.7 is that of five-year two-phase cycles, and regional market areas. This programme is estimated to cost Rs. 1,204 millions. For the most expensive programme (two-year single-phase cycles, and state market areas), the costs rise to Rs. 1,626 millions. This difference between the most and the least economical solutions is a rough measure of the price to be paid for haphazard decentralization of decisions on plant size, location and time-phasing.

TABLE 5.7

Present value of costs over infinite horizon, excluding proportional costs. Single- and two-phase cycles. (Rs. millions)

		Case 1 State market areas			Case 2 Regional market areas		
		Each individual state perpetually supplies itself			Regional centre perpetually supplies all states in region		
		I	T	I + T	I	T	I + T
Single-phase, five-year cycles	East	291	0	291	218	29	247
	North	279	0	279	205	26	231
	West	607	0	607	494	69	563
	South	336	0	336	247	41	288
	Total	1,513	0	1,513	1,164	165	1,329

		Regional centre alternates with other states in region			West alternates with three other regions		
		I	T	I + T	I	T	I + T
Two-phase, five-year cycles	East	255	2	257	171	36	207
	North	252	1	253	161	31	192
	West	536	6	542	494	69	563
	South	302	1	303	194	48	242
	Total	1,345	10	1,355	1,020	184	1,204

		Maharashtra alternates with 14 other states		
		I	T	I + T
Two-phase, five-year cycles	East	253	3	256
	North	242	2	244
	West	571	2	573
	South	292	2	294
	Total	1,358	9	1,367

Non-uniform proportional costs

It is now time to drop the assumption that the proportional costs are identical in all regions. Two alternatives are considered: (*a*) the South has a cost advantage of Rs. 70 per ton of caustic soda (equivalent to Rs. 0·02/kilowatt-hour of electricity consumption); or (*b*) the East has a cost advantage of Rs. 70 over all others.

In order to make direct comparisons with the previous results, we will restrict the possible programmes to the case of plants built to serve the national market area, with single-phase two-year cycles. In Table 5.8, the only alternative low-cost plant locations are Madras and West Bengal—depending upon whether the Southern or Eastern region happens to have the cost advantage. For reference purposes, Table 5.8 also includes a computation on serving the entire national market from the two high-cost locations: Delhi and Maharashtra.

TABLE 5.8

Effect of credit for proportional cost advantage

National market area.
One state perpetually supplies all states.
Single-phase, two-year cycles.

Present value of costs over infinite horizon
(Rs. millions)

	I	T	Credit for Rs. 70/ton proportional cost advantage	$I + T -$ credit
Low-cost suppliers				
Madras	926	537	−410	1,053
West Bengal	926	572	−410	1,088
High-cost suppliers				
Delhi Territory, U.P.—west	926	506	0	1,432
Maharashtra	926	382	0	1,308

Since the total output of all plants remains fixed at each point of time in the future, these calculations do not allow for the absolute level of the proportional costs but only for the *differential* of Rs. 70 per ton. In Table 5.8, this advantage for the Madras or West Bengal location is treated as a credit, a deduction from the investment and transport costs. The discounted value of this credit is reckoned as follows:

Present value
of Rs. 70/ton
cost advantage $= \int_{t=0}^{\infty} 70 \left(\sum_j D_j \right) t \, e^{-rt} \, dt$
over infinite
horizon

$$= 70 \frac{\left(\sum_j D_j \right)}{r^2} = \frac{70 \, (58 \cdot 6)}{(0 \cdot 10)^2} \text{ Rs. thousands}$$

$$= \text{Rs. 410 millions}$$

If any region were indeed to have a cost advantage of Rs. 70 per ton, Table 5.8 shows how enormously desirable it would be to concentrate the entire national production in that location. The differential in proportional costs makes it all the more desirable to take advantage of economies-of-scale, and to keep building new large plants in that region.

Plant size recommendations

In order to translate the preceding results into an action programme for the caustic soda industry, some attempt should be made to standardize the plant sizes. Throughout the preceding calculations, the advantages of standardization have been neglected. Plant sizes were set by fixing the market area to be served and also the cycle time between plants. (E.g. within the national market area, demand is growing at the annual rate of $58 \cdot 6$ thousand tons/year. With a two-year cycle time for serving that market, the plant size would be $117 \cdot 2 = 2(58 \cdot 6)$.) On this basis, two alternative sets of plant sizes would be recommended—depending upon the viewpoint adopted with respect to uniformity of the proportional costs:

Recommended Plant Size (thousands of tons/year)

	Uniform proportional costs (five-year, two-phase cycles); see Tables 5.2 and 5.7	Rs. 70/ton cost advantage for either the South or the East (two-year, single-phase cycles); see Tables 5.2 and 5.8
Region		
East	$49 \cdot 0$	$117 \cdot 2$
North	$45 \cdot 5$	0
West	$140 \cdot 5$	0
South	$58 \cdot 0$	$117 \cdot 2$

These numerical results happen to be compatible with standardization. In the uniform cost case, the recommended standard sizes could be 50 and 150 thousand tons/year. Alternatively, if a single region is presumed to have a cost advantage of Rs. 70/ton, the standard size could be 100 thousand tons/year.

Regardless of which assumption is made with respect to proportional costs, the model recommends larger unit sizes than those previously employed in India. The largest previous increment (Dhrangadhra) has been 28 thousand tons/year, while the recommended increments in capacity range from 50 thousand tons/year upwards.

The large plant sizes are recommended despite the biases against them in selecting the data inputs. If the calculations were modified to allow for economies-of-scale in operating labour and plant overheads, and if it were assumed that caustic soda is transported in a more concentrated form than 50% liquid, these changes would only strengthen the advantages of large versus small plants.

In India, it is often argued that plant sizes should be kept small—both for reasons of regional development and for promoting competition. According to our calculations, a substantial cost will have to be borne by the country if caustic soda plant decisions continue to be governed by these sentiments. For accomplishing the goals of anti-monopoly and of regional development, small plant sizes are neither a necessary nor a sufficient condition.

APPENDIX A

TABLE 5.9

State-wide distribution of caustic soda capacity
(thousand metric tons/year, 100% caustic soda)

State	January 1, 1961		January 1, 1964		January 1, 1966	
	Number of plants	Capacity	Number of plants	Capacity	Number of plants	Capacity
Andhra Pradesh	1	3·0	1	6·3	2	16·2
Bihar	1	5·6	1	5·6	1	12·2
Gajarat	3	35·0	3	27·7	4	36·3
Kerala	1	6·6	1	13·2	1	33·0
Madhya Pradesh	—	—	—	—	2	14·9
Madras	2	33·0	2	67·2	2	94·0
Maharashtra	3	13·6	3	18·8	5	46·3
Mysore	1	0·6	1	0·6	2	12·6
Orissa	1	3·2	1	3·2	2	19·7
Punjab (Delhi, J. & K.)	2	10·6	2	12·2	2	12·2
Rajasthan	—	—	1	16·5	1	16·5
Uttar Pradesh	—	—	—	—	1	16·5
West Bengal	3	12·8	3	16·6	4	30·4
Total	18	124·0	19	187·9	29	360·8

APPENDIX B

RAIL TARIFFS AND COSTS

The transport rates used in this study are based upon the existing tariff structure for Indian Railways. These rail charges depend only upon the commodity and the distance shipped—regardless of the gauge of the rail line, the density of traffic, the terrain, the frequency of back-hauls, or other factors that lead to variations in rail costs.

In India, no official estimates have yet been published of the cost to the railways of hauling individual commodities over various distances.[1] In the absence of such estimates, it is natural to raise two interrelated questions:

[1] There *are* official figures available on the cost per ton-mile of hauling the rails' most important single commodity, coal. (See Committee on Transport Policy and Coordination (1961, p. 78). Even in the case of coal, no estimate is available on the way in which the cost varies with the distance shipped.

(1) Does the general level of charges approximate the long-run marginal cost of hauling the product? (2) Does the pattern of 'telescoping' (increment in rate per unit increment in distance) reflect the long-run marginal costs? In answer to these questions, it is frequently asserted—but not readily proved—that: (1) the general level of rail rates for bulk commodities is too low, and (2) the telescoping pattern is tapered too sharply. According to this line of reasoning, it is concluded that the rail tariff structure gives an undue incentive to set up large plants for bulk commodities (e.g. caustic soda, cement, and fertilizers), and that these large plants are located too far away from their natural market areas.[1]

Undoubtedly, the Indian Railways deserve to be criticized for not having pushed their cost studies more energetically. One hopeful sign of a change is the fact that the Committee on Transport Policy and Co-ordination (1963) has published a review of foreign experience in railway rating and costing practices. The French experience is described in this review, and seems particularly relevant as an instance of progress in the direction of a cost-based rate structure.

It is safe to predict that at some time in the future the Indian Railways will also move in the direction of a cost-based rate structure. Meanwhile, for purposes of plant size and location decisions in the caustic soda

TABLE 5.10

Rail distances and charges

Rail distance, miles	Prevailing rail charges per bulk ton of caustic soda, including 10% surcharge	Extreme alternative, based on railways' average cost of Rs. 6·00/100 ton-miles, all commodities and distances
	Rs.	Rs.
100	10·78	6·00
200	17·07	12·00
300	23·06	18·00
400	27·84	24·00
500	32·93	30·00
600	36·83	36·00
700	41·02	42·00
800	44·91	48·00
900	48·51	54·00
1,000	52·10	60·00
1,100	55·69	66·00
1,200	58·98	72·00
1,300	61·99	78·00
1,400	64·98	84·00
1,500	67·97	90·00

[1] For a lively discussion of these issues, see J. M. Healey (1964).

industry, it seemed best to use the prevailing rail tariff. For those who are dissatisfied with this approach, Table 5.10 contains both the prevailing tariff structure and also an extreme alternative form. According to this alternative, the rail rates for all commodities and all distances should be set at the railways' average cost of Rs. 6.00/100 ton miles.[1] On the basis of some side calculations, it can be seen that not even the extreme alternative rail tariff structure would alter the general conclusions of this chapter.

REFERENCES

Committee on Transport Policy and Coordination, *Preliminary Report*, Government of India, February 1961.

Committee on Transport Policy and Coordination, *Railway policies before and since Independence and some of the present-day problems and Railway Rating Policy in some of the Foreign Countries*, Government of India, August 1963.

Healey, J. M., 'An Analysis of Railway Costs and Prices', *The Economic Weekly*, January 1964.

Perspective Planning Division, 'Development of Chemical Industry: 1960–1970', Planning Commission, New Delhi, May 1963.

United Nations, Economic Commission for Latin America, *La Industria Química en América Latina*, E/CN. 12/628/Rev. 1, New York, 1963.

[1] The average cost figure of Rs. 6·00/100 ton-miles was suggested as a rough approximation in Committee on Transport Policy and Coordination (1961, p. 87).

CHAPTER 6

THE CEMENT INDUSTRY

ALAN S. MANNE[1]

Summary

This analysis of the cement industry applies both the single- and the two-phase models for multiple producing areas. The chapter begins by outlining the basic data inputs: capital and operating costs, limestone availability, statewide demands for cement, and transport costs. Each of these elements required a combination of both judgment and objective facts. On the basis of the data that appeared most reasonable, the model yields the following policy recommendations:

(1) In this industry—unlike caustic soda—transport costs are high. There are only modest gains to be had from temporary shifts in market boundaries between adjacent limestone-bearing states.

(2) There is little justification for continuing to license plants with kiln sizes of 100 thousand tons per year. Except for Jammu and Kashmir, these seem too small in relation to statewide demands and yet too large to serve isolated, remote areas.

(3) Currently, the manufacture of cement plants is being introduced into India on the basis of standard-sized kilns, each with an annual capacity of 200 thousand tons.[2] From the viewpoint of the cement plant operators, it appears considerably more economical if this standard size could be increased to 400 or even 600 thousand tons.

(4) Undoubtedly, there would be technical difficulties in switching over to the larger-sized units. Since the larger kilns are more awkward to transport from the manufacturing shops to the cement plant sites, the industry would have to learn how to do a greater proportion of on-site welding than for the smaller units. Moreover, the manufacturers of cement plant equipment would be faced with even

---

[1] The author is indebted to T. R. Talwar for the cement demand estimates, and to P. N. Radhakrishnan and T. V. S. Rao for assistance with the numerical analysis.

[2] Even though the kiln size has been standardized at 200 thousand tons, this does not mean that *designs* have been standarized. Each of four Indian equipment manufacturers utilizes a design by a different foreign collaborator. See Khatau (1964).

smaller and more erratic production runs than is already the case for kilns of 200 thousand tons. Surely this conflict between the equipment manufacturers and the users is not unique to the cement industry. In order for India to build large plants economically, a substantial reorganization of the engineering industries may be indicated: a smaller number of designs of complete plants, less vertical integration of the process of producing equipment, more sub-contracting back and forth between shops with specialized skills and equipment, and with general coordination being exercised by firms that design complete plants suited to the needs of the using industry.

Capital and operating costs for a standard-sized plant

Table 6.1 contains the best information available to us on the cost of manufacturing cement in India. These are taken from V. Podder (1962, p. 376). The numbers shown here are those applicable to a standard-sized new cement plant centred around a single kiln with an annual capacity of 200 thousand tons.

In Table 6.1, the inputs have been classified into two types: those proportional to output and those subject to economies-of-scale. In the second category, only money values are specified. In the first category both money and physical inputs are given. From Table 6.1 alone—without a detailed consideration of the location of demand—it is safe to draw a number of immediate conclusions concerning the location of cement plants:

(1) This is a weight-losing process; it takes $1 \cdot 45$ tons of limestone per ton of cement. Since the transport costs of cement are less than 45% above those of limestone, the conversion process ought to take place in the immediate vicinity of limestone quarries.[1]

(2) Fuel and power are significant elements of cost in this process (Rs. $11 \cdot 2 + 7 \cdot 2$ out of the ex-works cost of Rs. $62 \cdot 8$ per ton of cement, according to Podder). Regional differences in fuel and power costs *might* have an influence on cement plant size, location and time-phasing.

(3) In order to simplify the data needed for our model, we shall continue to suppose that all production and all demand within each individual state takes place at a single representative point—either

[1] It is possible to divorce the manufacture of cement into two stages at separate locations: first the conversion of limestone into clinker and second the grinding of clinker into cement. All of the weight loss takes place at the first step, and clinker can be transported towards the market more cheaply than cement. Nevertheless, since an overwhelming majority of the manufacturing cost is incurred in producing clinker, this paper ignores the possibility of divorcing the two steps.

the largest or most centrally located city. (Refer back to Table 4.2.) The distance between adjacent points ranges from 310 to 690 kilometres. Now according to Podder's data for a standard-sized new plant (Table 6.1), those operating and capital costs subject to

TABLE 6.1

Cost of production of cement*
(single-kiln plant with output of 200 thousand metric tons/year)

	Unit consumption	Rs./metric ton of cement
Operating costs—proportional to output		
Limestone†	1·45 tons	8·8
Flue dust	0·04 ,,	1·0
Gypsum	0·04 ,,	2·0
Coal	0·25 ,,	11·2
Power	120 kwhrs.	7·2
Sub-total		30·2
Operating costs—subject to economies-of-scale		
Spare parts and refractories		3·0
Repair and maintenance		3·0
Labour		4·6
Staff		2·0
Overhead		6·0
Sub-total		18·6
Capital costs—subject to economies-of-scale		
Depreciation at 8%/year on initial investment of Rs. 35 millions		14·0
Total, ex-works		62·8‡

NOTES:

* Source: Podder (1962, p. 376).

† It is quite probable that there are economies-of-scale in limestone quarrying —provided that mechanization is employed rather than hand methods. In order to err on the safe side, no credit has been taken here for economies-of-scale in quarrying.

‡ In Podder, there is a minor misprint, and this total is shown as Rs. 62·3.

economies-of-scale amount to Rs. 18·6 + 14·0 = Rs. 32·6 per ton of cement. If, by serving a wider area, a larger-sized plant would make it possible to cut these unit costs in half, the saving of Rs. 16 in manufacturing costs would pay for shipping cement an extra distance of approximately 500 kilometres. This break-even distance is of the same order of magnitude as the distances between adjacent representative points in the various states. This rough calculation is

G

sufficient to rule out much interest in the possibility that one state's cement plant—no matter how large—would *permanently* serve a market in any other limestone-bearing state. This initial calculation does not, however, permit us to rule out interstate shipments altogether. They may be needed permanently because a state has no limestone deposits close to its principal markets. Or they may be useful temporarily while one state has built a large new plant ahead of its own internal demand.

Economies-of-scale in capital and operating costs

In order to extrapolate costs to kiln sizes of other than 200 thousand tons, we have used an economies-of-scale parameter $a = 0·68$. This implies that for kilns of twice and three times the standard size, the total costs subject to economies-of-scale are, respectively $1·60$ and $2·11$ times those for kilns of 200 thousand tons.[1]

The value of $0·68$ for the economies-of-scale parameter is taken from a curve of the initial *fixed investment* costs only, as estimated for 'developing countries' in a report published by the United Nations (1963). This report goes on to state that the exponent for cement plant capital costs varies from $0·64$ in a set of German data, $0·66$ in USSR data, and $0·77$ for the United States.

As far as India is concerned, there is no evidence that the exponent of $0·68$ overstates the extent of economies-of-scale in capital costs. Within the restricted range of kiln sizes considered by Podder (167 to 250 thousand tons), he estimates that the initial investment cost for a new unit goes from Rs. $30·7$ to $38·2$ millions.[2] This would correspond to a scaling exponent of $0·54$, far greater economies-of-scale than indicated by the UN reports.[3]

In the case of those *operating* costs subject to economies-of-scale, (spare parts, maintenance, labour, staff and overhead), it is likely that the appropriate scaling exponent is even lower than the value of $0·68$. A rough confirmation of this has been obtained from two Indian multi-plant regression analyses: one for the year 1959 and one for 1962.[4] (Note that these data refer to multi-kiln plants.) Here

[1] In the opinion of one Indian manufacturer, an exponent of roughly $0·7$ would apply even up to a kiln size of 800 thousand tons.

[2] Podder (1962, pp. 75, 76).

[3] Although the various sources differ from each other in estimating the extent of economies-of-scale, they do not differ greatly in the absolute level of investment costs. At a plant size of 200 thousand tons, Podder gives a figure of Rs. 35 millions for a new unit; the UN report gives a range of Rs. 33 to 38 millions (converting at the official exchange rate of Rs. $4·75 = \$1·00$); and Perspective Planning Division (1964, Table M) sets the cost of a new unit at Rs. 32 millions.

[4] The raw data on cement production and man-hours per ton are taken from an

the independent variable x represents the plant's total production during the particular year (measured in thousands of metric tons), and the dependent variable y represents the man-hours per ton of production for that plant.

The linear regression estimates for the two sample years are as follows:[1]

1959:	$\log y = 2 \cdot 17 - 0 \cdot 49 \log x$
Standard error of regression coefficient	$= \pm 0 \cdot 16$
R^2	$= 0 \cdot 34$
1962:	$\log y = 1 \cdot 93 - 0 \cdot 39 \log x$
Standard error of regression coefficient	$= \pm 0 \cdot 12$
R^2	$= 0 \cdot 30$

From this log-linear formulation in terms of the labour input per unit of production, it is possible to show that the economies-of-scale parameter a for the total labour inputs may be estimated as follows:

$$\text{1959 sample: } a = 1 \cdot 00 - 0 \cdot 49 = 0 \cdot 51$$

$$\text{1962 sample: } a = 1 \cdot 00 - 0 \cdot 39 = 0 \cdot 61$$

Since the regression coefficients have sizeable standard errors ($\pm 0 \cdot 16$ and $\pm 0 \cdot 12$), these estimates of a are not statistically significantly different from the capital cost exponent $a = 0 \cdot 68$. Hence the economies-of-scale parameter of $0 \cdot 68$ has been adopted both for the operating and for the capital costs.

Costs of new units and substantial expansions

In estimating the costs subject to economies-of-scale, it appears important to distinguish those associated with 'new units' from those for 'substantial expansions'. Physically, the sequence of events in the

unpublished manuscript by Pareshnath Chatterjee (1963). In order to make the sample more homogeneous, all observations were omitted for those plants operating at less than 70% of capacity during the particular year. For 1959 and 1962, this left 20 and 28 plants respectively in the sample.

[1] Logarithms are taken to the base 10.

cement industry seems to be as follows. At the time the first kiln is constructed at a given location, provision is ordinarily made for doubling the plant's size at a later date. E.g. the initially constructed slurry basin and the stack might be designed large enough to serve a second kiln when and if it gets constructed. The railway siding and the materials handling facilities might also be designed so as to be capable of serving a second kiln.

This can all be summed up by saying that some excess capacity is initially built into the units ancillary to the kiln. These ancillary units cannot, however, be stretched indefinitely to serve a fourth, fifth, and sixth kiln. For the sake of definiteness, we shall suppose that the plant has been designed exactly so that the ancillary units will serve two kilns but no more. Following Podder (1962, pp. 75, 76), the investment costs for all equipment associated with the second kiln are taken at 75% those for the first. At each location, it is supposed that a new unit is followed by *one* substantial expansion.

The individual cost components are now ready to be combined for use in the plant size optimization model. For this purpose, it is convenient to work with a single total for the present value of constructing, replacing and operating in perpetuity. The numbers in Table 6.2a refer to a new unit with a kiln capacity of 200 thousand tons/year. Those in Table 6.2b have been derived from Table 6.2a using the 75% factor for an expansion and the scaling exponent of

TABLE 6.2a

Costs of a new 200 thousand tons/year plant

Cost component	Rs. millions over specified time interval	Rs. millions, present worth, discounting in perpetuity at 10% per annum, compounded continuously
Initial investment	35·0 once for all time	35·0
Replacement of initial investment	35·0 every 18 years*	7·0
Operating costs (spare parts, maintenance, labour, staff, and overhead)	3·72 per year†	37·2
Total present value		79·2

NOTES:
  * In terms of equation (2.6), the replacement factor $\rho = 1·20$.
  † From Table 6.1.

TABLE 6.2b

Extrapolation of costs to 'substantial expansions' and to kiln sizes other than 200 thousand tons/year

Kiln size (thousand tons/year)	200	400	600
Cost of a new unit, total present value (Rs. millions)	79·2	126·7	167·1
Cost of a substantial expansion, total present value (Rs. millions)	59·4	95·0	125·3

0·68 for kilns of larger sizes. In general, letting xD = kiln size (thousands of tons/year):

Cost of a new unit
(Rs. millions) $= f(xD) = 79 \cdot 2 \left(\frac{xD}{200}\right)^{0 \cdot 68}$

Cost of a substantial
expansion (Rs. millions) $= 0 \cdot 75 f(xD) = 59 \cdot 4 \left(\frac{xD}{200}\right)^{0 \cdot 68}$

Reinterpreting the symbols used in previous chapters:

D = annual increase in demand within a given market area ((thousands of tons/year)/year)

x = time interval between successive kilns (years)

xD = kiln size (thousands of tons/year)

r = annual discount rate, compounded continuously (1/year)

Every x years over an infinite horizon, a kiln is to be built to serve a given market area. The first of these is a new kiln, the second a substantial expansion, the third a new kiln, and so on. Analogous to equation (2.5), the discounted value of all future investment and operating costs subject to economies-of-scale in cement manufacturing, is as follows:

$$C(x) \atop \text{(Rs. millions)} = \frac{\left[\dfrac{xD}{200}\right]^{0 \cdot 68} [79 \cdot 2 + e^{-rx} 59 \cdot 4]}{1 - e^{-2rx}} \qquad (6.1)$$

Limestone availability

Figure 6.1, a map of the Indian cement industry, indicates the location of each of the 16 representative points at which both consumption and production are supposedly concentrated. (There is one representative point for each state in the Union, excluding Nagaland and including Delhi Territory.) The figure also indicates the location

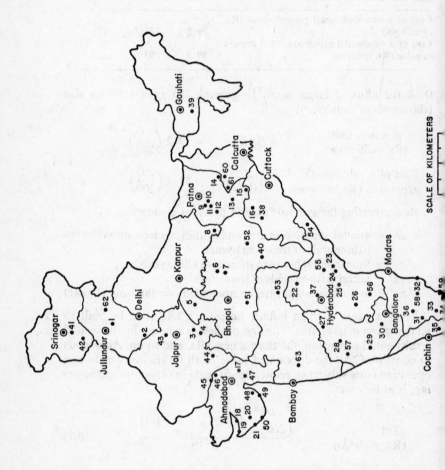

Annual capacity of cement factories, January 1, 1964
(thousands of metric tons)

Existing units

		Annual capacity
1.	Surajpur	406
2.	Dalmia Dadri	239
3.	Sawaimadhopur	819
4.	Lakheri	366
5.	Banmore	61
6.	Satna	251
7.	Kymore	582
8.	Churk	235
9.	Dalmianagar (A)	284
10.	Dalmianagar (B)	335
11.	Banjari	146
12.	Japla	254
13.	Khalari	102
14.	Sindri	305
15.	Chaibasa	488
16.	Rajgangpur	371
17.	Sevalia	203
18.	Sikka	437
19.	Dwarka	223
20.	Eamavar	203
21.	Porbandar	43
22.	Mancherial	335
23.	Vijawada	201
24.	Kistna	259
25.	Macherla	254
26.	Cement Nagar	64
27.	Shahabad	574
28.	Bagalkot	203
29.	Bhadravati	100
30.	Tumkur	102
31.	Madukkarai	284
32.	Dalmiapuram	419
33.	Talukappatti	67
34.	Talaiyuthu	463
35.	Kottayam	51
		9,729

New units and substantial expansions

			Annual capacity
6.	Satna	S.E.	274
7.	Kymore	S.E.	25
8.	Churk	S.E.	235
11.	Banjari	S.E.	101
18.	Sikka	S.E.	203
19.	Dwarka	S.E.	117
21.	Porbandar	S.E.	125
26.	Cement Nagar	New	134
30.	Tumkur	New	102
31.	Madukkarai	S.E.	122
33.	Talukappatti	S.E.	134
36.	Sankaridrug	New	168
37.	Bhongir	New	168
38.	Sambalpur	New	396
39.	Cherrapunji	New	84
40.	Jamul	New	168
41.	Wuyan	New	20
			2,576

Licensed-approved (new cement factories for which arrangements for machinery are to be made)

			Annual capacity
9.	Dalmianagar	S.E.	223
12.	Japla	S.E.	235
	(Slag cement)		
16.	Rajgangpur	S.E.	173
42.	Riasi	New	366
43.	Nian Ka Thana	New	203
44.	Chitorgarh	New	203
45.	Abu Road	New	168
46.	Pasina	New	168
47.	Baroda	New	203
48.	Bhavanagar	New	102
49.	Port Albert Victor	New	51
50.	Veraval	New	168
51.	Bhanpura	New	51
52.	Champa	New	203
53.	Rajpur	New	168
54.	Vizianagaram	New	203
55.	Bonakalu	New	203
56.	Yerraguntla	New	198
57.	Nagargali	New	203
58.	Karur	New	168
59.	Rameswaram	New	168
60.	Durgapur	New	244
61.	Jhalda	New	203
62.	Samloti	New	102
63.	Hadaspor	New	102
			4,682

and capacity of each cement plant existing on January 1, 1964, together with the new units and substantial expansions that had been licensed as of that date.

No complete geological survey of India's cement-grade limestone deposits has yet been published. However, since each of the existing and licensed cement plants is adjacent to a commercial deposit, Figure 6.1 can also serve as a rough-and-ready indicator of the country's known reserves. It is significant that no sizeable cement plants lie within the immediate vicinity of five of the major centres of consumption: Calcutta, Bombay, Delhi, Kanpur and Cochin. This could be interpreted as a lack of rationality in locational decisions on the part of the cement industry.[1] An alternative explanation (the viewpoint adopted here) is that cement-grade limestone deposits are not ubiquitous in India, and are not available at these specific points. In our model, it is therefore supposed that cement production cannot be carried on at any of the five locations just listed, and that future increments in demand will be met by imports from neighbouring states. Note that the absence of limestone in certain locations enlarges the natural market area—hence favours larger plant sizes— for their limestone-bearing neighbours.

Demand forecasts

Both exports and imports are excluded from this study. Table 6.3 contains the state-by-state forecasts of domestic demand used here. Appendix A described the general methodology underlining these projections. For each major type of construction activity, a state-by-state investment target has been estimated for the terminal years of the Third and Fourth Plan periods, 1965–66 and 1970–71 respectively. On the basis of cement norms per million rupees' worth of investment, the investment targets have been translated into tonnage requirements for cement.

The demand forecast of Table 6.3 implies an increase of approximately 10% per year compounded annually over the Fourth Plan. The rate of increase depends almost entirely upon what is assumed with respect to investment activity during this period. Any rise or drop in the aggregate investment target will have a virtually proportional impact upon the demand for cement.

In judging the reasonableness of the demand forecasts, some note should be taken of the fact that during the entire Third Plan period,

---

[1] The existing system of price controls (uniform ex-works prices to all plants operated by a single enterprise) provides no financial incentive for a manufacturer to locate a new plant nearby his markets. See Podder (1962, pp. 95–98) for the Tariff Commission's pricing formula for 1961–64.

TABLE 6.3

Statewise cement dispatches*
(thousands of metric tons)

	1960–61 actual	1965–66 forecast	1970–71 forecast	Average annual increase in demand during Fourth Plan
East				
Assam	194	500	815	63
Bihar	656	1,333	2,174	168
Orissa	311	708	1,155	89
West Bengal	719	1,194	1,948	151
North				
Delhi Territory	236	280	453	35
Punjab	640	667	1,087	84
Rajasthan	194	778	1,268	98
West-Central				
Gujarat ⎱	1,578	861	1,404	109
Maharashtra ⎰		1,347	2,197	170
Madhya Pradesh	463	1,375	2,242	173
Uttar Pradesh	848	1,625	2,650	205‡
South				
Andhra Pradesh	574	1,000	1,631	126
Kerala	167	570	929	72
Madras	713	653	1,064	82
Mysore	432	861	1,404	109
Total†	7,725	13,752	22,421	1,734

NOTES:

* Source: Unpublished estimates by T. R. Talwar, Perspective Planning Division, Planning Commission.

† Excludes minor quantities for the Union Territories of Tripura, Manipur, Goa, Daman, Diu, Himachal Pradesh, Pondicherry, Andaman, Nicobar, Laccadive and Minicoy Islands, and the states of Nagaland, Jammu and Kashmir. In 1960–61, these areas received 82 thousand tons of cement.

‡ In subsequent calculations, the demands of Uttar Pradesh are split up, with 60% allocated to U.P.—east and 40% to U.P.—west. Among the state's cities with 1961 population in excess of 100,000 persons, there is a 60–40 division of population between those that are closer to Kanpur and those closer to Delhi.

demand has tended to exceed the supply at the official prices, cement has been rationed by administrative fiat, and there has been an active black market at prices above the legal ceilings.

Cost comparisons, single-phase cycles, excluding transport costs

With the exception of transport costs, the data inputs have now been described: state-by-state forecasts of the rate of growth of demand, the economies-of-scale relationship for plant investment and operating costs, and the assumptions with respect to limestone deficit areas. Cost comparisons are made in terms of the discounted present value over an infinite horizon, using a continuously compounded discount rate of 10% per annum. In order to allow for alternation between new units and substantial expansions, cost equation (6.1) is applied.

Transport costs are omitted from the comparison since they are unaffected by the choice of kiln size. That is, in the single-phase model, the decision problem is one of choosing the best kiln size for meeting state-by-state demands. Unlike the two-phase model, it is supposed that each state's entire demand for cement is permanently met from a single source of supply—either that state itself or its nearest limestone-bearing neighbour.[1] Transport costs are therefore fixed by the location of the point of supply together with the predetermined rate of growth of demand within the market area assigned to that source. These elements are independent of *when* the plants are built and what their size happens to be.

In Table 6.4, cost comparisons are made between three standard kiln sizes: 200, 400 and 600 thousand tons/year. The highest of these sizes lies below the 800 thousand ton capacity of the largest existing kilns in the world. The lowest size is the standard one being licensed by India for most of the new units and expansions of the Fourth Plan. (See Figure 6.1 above.) Note that in every market area—with the exception of Assam—the minimum discounted costs are achieved with the *largest* of the three standard sizes considered here. If it turns out to be impractical to take advantage of this size within India, a second-best alternative (one which still captures most of the economies-of-scale) might be to adopt 400 thousand tons as the standard kiln.

Transport costs

If a cement plant is constantly employed to serve a predetermined market area (its home state and its limestone deficit neighbours), it has already been argued that an optimal plant size can be chosen without regard to the costs of interstate transport. Transport costs are unaffected by the choice of plant size. If however, the units are programmed to make temporary but not permanent shipments across state boundary lines, the cost comparison becomes more

[1] Since there is only one representative point of production and consumption for each state, the model omits intrastate transport costs altogether.

TABLE 6.4

Cost comparisons; effect of alternative kiln sizes; single-phase cycles

| | East | | | North | | West-Central | | South | | | |
	Assam	Orissa	Bihar + W. Bengal	Punjab	Rajasthan + Delhi + U.P., west	M.P. + U.P., east‡	Gujarat + Maharashtra	Andhra Pradesh	Mysore + Kerala	Madras	Total
Annual increase in demand (thousands of metric tons)	63	89	319	84	215	296	279	126	181	82	1,734
Present value of costs (millions of Rs.; discounting at 10%/year)* Kiln size 200 (thousand tons/year)	261	350	1,145	333	785	1,066	1,007	477	668	326	6,418
400	246†	316	949	302	659	886	838	417	568	297	5,478
600	253	311†	864†	300†	608†	809†	767†	398†	530†	294†	5,134

NOTES: * Calculated according to equation (6.1).

† Optimal choice among 3 sizes.

‡ Both Patna and Jaipur are slightly closer to Kanpur than is Bhopal. Nevertheless, M.P. is taken as the source of supply for UP, east. There are major limestone deposits in M.P. within 400 kilometres of Kanpur.

complex. An allowance must be made for transport costs—both of the cement product and also of the fuel and power inputs to the process.

The transport rates shown in Table 6.5 are those applicable to rail shipments of cement and of coal in wagon loads.[1] Note that the

TABLE 6.5
Railway freight rates
(wagon loads; including 10% surcharge, 1964)

Miles	Rate per metric ton of cement	Kilometres	Rate per metric ton of coal
50	7·18	1– 70	5·50
100	10·78	71– 150	7·04
150	14·07	151– 200	8·80
200	17·07	201– 250	10·42
250	20·06	251– 300	12·18
300	23·06	301– 350	13·47
350	25·45	351– 400	14·21
400	27·84	401– 450	15·09
450	30·24	451– 500	16·04
500	32·93	501– 550	16·79
600	36·83	551– 600	17·53
700	41·02	601– 650	18·47
800	44·91	651– 700	19·22
900	48·51	701– 750	19·82
1,000	52·10	751– 800	20·57
1,100	55·69	801– 850	21·32
1,200	58·98	851– 900	21·92
1,300	61·99	901– 950	22·67
1,400	64·98	951–1,000	23·49
1,500	67·97	1,001–1,100	24·84
		1,101–1,200	26·32
Above 1,500 miles, add Rs. 0·90 per		1,201–1,300	27·32
ton for each additional 100 miles.		1,301–1,400	28·21
		1,401–1,500	29·23
		1,501–1,600	30·17
		1,601–1,700	30·92
		1,701–1,800	31·87
		1,801–1,900	32·60
		1,901–2,000	33·42
		2,001–2,100	34·44
		2,101–2,200	35·18
		2,201–2,300	35·93
		2,301 and above	36·66

[1] For calculating *inter*state transport of these two commodities, there is probably no great error in neglecting modes of transport other than rail. During April–June 1962, the tonnage of cement dispatched by road was only 4% of the combined total of road and rail for distances over 300 kilometres. See Joint Technical Group on Transport Planning (1963, p. 9).

Indian rail tariff structure depends only upon the commodity and the distance shipped—regardless of the gauge of the rail line, the density of traffic, the terrain, the frequency of back-hauls, or other factors that lead to variations in rail costs. The coal tariff structure has been subject to particularly heavy criticism. (See J. M. Healey (1964).) It is widely asserted—but not readily proved—that: (1) The general level of charges is below the long-run marginal costs of hauling coal. (2) The pattern of 'telescoping' (increment in rate per unit increment in distance) is unduly favourable to long distance shipping of coal.

To date, critics of the rail tariff structure have contented themselves with literary assaults rather than serious attempts to measure the railways' costs. Since most of the controversy has centred around coal and not cement, our cost comparisons for haulage of cement are based upon the conventional rate structure for this commodity. For transport of coal, however, two alternatives have been computed: In one case, coal haulage was charged up at the conventional rate structure, and in the other at the rate-distance structure prevailing for cement. In this second case, the effect is a substantial increase in the general level of coal haulage rates and a reduction in the telescoping with distance.

TABLE 6.6

Rail freight rates
(Rs. per metric ton, including 10% surcharge)

Origin	Destination	Cement rate Rs.	Coal rate Rs.
Patna, Bihar	Gauhati, Assam	26·90	17·93
,, ,,	Cuttack, Orissa	36·24	22·67
,, ,,	Calcutta, West Bengal	24·97	—
,, ,,	Jullundur, Punjab	—	24·84
,, ,,	Jaipur, Rajasthan	—	23·13
,, ,,	Ahmadabad, Gujarat	—	30·17
,, ,,	Bhopal, Madhya Pradesh	—	22·95
,, ,,	Hyderabad, Andhra Pradesh	—	31·74
,, ,,	Bangalore, Mysore	—	36·66
,, ,,	Madras, Madras	—	35·18
Jaipur, Rajasthan	Delhi Territory	16·45	—
,, ,,	Jullundur, Punjab	28·80	—
Bhopal, Madhya Pradesh	Kanpur, Uttar Pradesh	24·97	—
,, ,,	Bombay, Maharashtra	33·71	—
Ahmadabad, Gujarat	Bombay, Maharashtra	23·20	—
Bangalore, Mysore	Hyderabad, Andhra Pradesh	29·33	—
,, ,,	Cochin, Kerala	27·17	—
,, ,,	Madras, Madras	18·33	—

Coal and cement transport rates between the various representative points are shown in Table 6.6. These rates have been derived by applying the tariff structure of Table 6.5 to the interstate rail distances specified in Table 4.2. Throughout the country, we have chosen to price out coal transport *as though* all coal originated at Patna, Bihar.[1]

One further note on the subject of coal: The input norm used here is $0 \cdot 32$ tons of coal per ton of cement production. This allows for $0 \cdot 25$ tons of coal directly as fuel for the cement plant plus an additional $0 \cdot 07$ tons for a thermal electric plant to generate 120 kilowatt-hours. (See Table 6.1 above.) The coal norm of $0 \cdot 32$ tons is adopted for the sake of simplicity—even though it ignores a number of realistic but partially offsetting details: (1) There has been a trend towards using coal of higher ash content—hence hauling more tons of bulk per kilocalorie produced. (2) Some of the southern and western cement plants are fired by fuel oil rather than coal. (3) In some areas of India, the primary source of power is hydroelectric rather than coal-based thermal plants.

Cost comparisons, single- and two-phase cycles

Depending upon the magnitude of transport costs, it may be worthwhile to build a large manufacturing unit in one state, temporarily allocate its capacity to supply itself and its neighbours, and thereafter permanently allocate the plant's capacity to supply its home state alone. In Chapter 4, we referred to this pattern as 'two-phase cycles'. Through this time sequence, we benefit by *deferring* construction in the neighbouring states but incur the penalty of transport costs during the initial phase of the cycle. In this section, we compare the total discounted costs of single- with two-phase cycles for the cement industry.

In view of the high cost of transporting cement relative to its cost of manufacture, only one form of two-phase cycle is considered here: state market areas, the regional centre alternating with other states in the region. (See Table 6.7.) E.g. the eastern region includes four states: Assam, Bihar, Orissa, and West Bengal. The regional centre is Bihar. It perpetually supplies both its own demands for cement and also those of West Bengal, a limestone deficit state. In the terminology of Chapter 4, area 1 consists of Bihar and West Bengal; area 2 consists of Assam and Orissa.

[1] One justification for this Patna-plus system of coal prices is that it is roughly consistent with the dual variables to the linear programming solution described in Indian Statistical Institute (1963, p. 38).

TABLE 6.7

Idealized time sequence of construction programme;
two-phase cycles; state market areas

Region	Time (years)	Number of kilns built	Size of kiln (thousands of tons/year)	Producing location	Annual increment in demand within market area normally served by this producing location (thousands of tons)
East	0*	1	600	Bihar‡	319
	1·27	1	600	,,	
	2·55	1	600	,,	
	3·82	1	600	,,	
	5·10†	2	237	Assam	63
	5·10	2	335	Orissa	89
	7·52*				—
				Regional total	471
North	0*	1	600	Rajasthan‡	215
	2·00	1	600	,,	
	4·00	1	600	,,	
	6·00	1	600	,,	
	8·00†	2	470	Punjab	84
	11·16*				—
				Regional total	299
West-Central	0*	1	600	Madhya Pradesh‡§	296
	1·04	1	600	,,	
	2·09†	2	565	Gujarat	279
	1·05*				—
				Regional total	575
South	0*	1	600	Mysore‡	181
	1·54	1	600	,,	
	3·08†	2	418	Andhra Pradesh	126
	3·08	2	272	Madras	82
	6·63*				—
				Regional total	389

NOTES:
* Begin phase 1 of new cycle.
† End phase 1 and begin phase 2 of this cycle.
‡ This producing location is the regional centre.
§ During phase 1, Madhya Pradesh satisfies the demand increase in *both* Gujarat and Maharashtra by shipping cement into the latter. This permits a transport cost saving on the normal flow from Gujarat to Maharashtra.

Within the eastern region, the total cycle time ($7 \cdot 52$ years) is determined by the period it takes for the demand in area 1 to grow by a sufficient amount to fill up the capacity of four large kilns (each with an annual output of 600 thousand tons) installed in Bihar. During the first phase within the cycle ($5 \cdot 10$ years), area 1 supplies both itself and area 2. The duration of this phase is set by the time it takes for the *combined* demand throughout the eastern region to grow by an amount equal to the capacity of the four large kilns in Bihar.[1]

Table 6.8 contains a regional cost summary for each of the four possibilities: single-phase and two-phase cycles; coal transport at coal rates and at cement rates. For single-phase cycles, note that the manufacturing costs are identical with those at the optimal kiln sizes already given in Table 6.4. For two-phase cycles, the manufacturing and transport costs are those implied by the time sequence in Table 6.7. The general results of these calculations may be summarized as follows:

(1) Regardless of which rate structure applies to the transport of coal, there are only modest gains in utilizing two-phase rather than single-phase cycles.[2] Unlike what was found in the caustic soda industry, here almost all of the savings in manufacturing are dissipated in the additional costs of transporting the product.[3]

(2) Although the rate structure assumed for coal transport has a

[1] A number of alternatives to the time-phasing patterns of Table 6.7 were considered, but rejected upon further consideration. Each of these possibilities might be worth investigation if the computations were being performed on an electronic computer rather than by hand: (1) There are two states (Assam and Madras) in which the kiln size turns out to be less than 300 thousand tons, i.e. less than half the largest size considered technologically feasible here. During each cycle, it would be possible to construct one large rather than two small kilns in these states. (2) In the eastern and northern regions, it would save on transport costs if two rather than four large kilns were built in area 1 during the first phase of each cycle. This pattern has the economic disadvantage, however, of halving the cycle time, hence halving the kiln size in area 2. (3) Whenever the duration of the first phase is less than *half* the total cycle time, it is not necessary to build both a new unit and a substantial expansion simultaneously in area 2. The second kiln for area 2 can be deferred until a later point through the overall cycle. This possibility exists in the southern region, but would hardly make any difference in the numerical results.

[2] This does not rule out investigations into more complex periodicities than two-phase cycles. From Table 6.7, one can see that outside the regional centre the kilns tend to be smaller than is technologically feasible and also non-standard in size.

[3] This conclusion checks with that obtained by somewhat different methods in Ghosh (1965, ch. VII).

TABLE 6.8

Cost comparisons; effect of time-phasing and of coal transport rates
(present value of costs; millions of Rs.; discounting at 10%/year)

	Region	Single-phase cycles				Two-phase cycles			
		Manu-facturing costs*	Transport of cement	Transport of coal	Total	Manu-facturing costs*	Transport of cement	Transport of coal	Total
Coal transport at conventional rates for coal	East	1,421	377	101	1,899	1,330	464	83	1,877
	North	908	192	226	1,326	836	262	225	1,323
	West-Central	1,576	702	487	2,765	1,525	718	483	2,726
	South	1,222	196	433	1,851	1,175	237	435	1,847
	Total	5,127	1,467	1,247	7,841	4,866	1,681	1,226	7,773
Coal transport at rates for cement	East	1,421	377	158	1,956	1,330	464	130	1,924
	North	908	192	360	1,460	836	262	358	1,456
	West-Central	1,576	702	809	3,087	1,525	718	801	3,044
	South	1,222	196	832	2,250	1,175	237	836	2,248
	Total	5,127	1,467	2,159	8,753	4,866	1,681	2,125	8,672

NOTE: * Includes only those elements of manufacturing cost subject to economies-of-scale.

H

significant effect upon the absolute level of cement costs, it has virtually no effect upon the *difference* in costs between two-phase and single-phase cycles. Apparently this lack of interaction occurs because coal has to be transported from Patna to the identical region of the country—regardless of whether the production of cement takes place directly in the consuming state or whether it takes place at the regional centre during phase 1 of each cycle.

Cost per ton of cement

For those readers who are unaccustomed to present value calculations, it seems a worthwhile exercise to translate Table 6.8 back into more familiar terms: rupees per ton of cement. In order to perform this translation, it is convenient to use the following symbols:

D = annual increase in cement demand within India = $1 \cdot 734$ (millions of tons/year)/year

t = an arbitrary future point in time (years)

tD = cement demand (and output) within India at time t (millions of tons/year)

e^{-rt} = present worth factor for time t, discounting continuously at the annual rate $r = 0 \cdot 10$/year

c = (unknown) equivalent cost per ton of cement demand and output (Rs./ton)

Present value of manufacturing costs shown in Table 6.8 (millions of Rs.)

$$= \int_{t=0}^{\infty} (ctD)e^{-rt}dt = \frac{cD}{r^2} \quad \cdot \quad \cdot \quad \cdot \quad (6.2)$$

$$\therefore \ 5127 = \frac{cD}{r^2}$$

$$\text{or} \quad c = \frac{5{,}127\,r^2}{D} = \frac{5{,}127\,(0 \cdot 10)^2}{1 \cdot 734}$$

$$c = \text{Rs. } 29 \cdot 6/\text{ton of cement}$$

The figure of Rs. $29 \cdot 6$ per ton of cement includes only those manufacturing costs that are subject to economies-of-scale: initial investment, replacement, spare parts, maintenance, labour, staff and overhead. Roughly speaking, it is comparable with the cost of $18 \cdot 6 + 14 \cdot 0 = $ Rs. $32 \cdot 6$ per ton taken from Podder and shown for these items in Table 6.1. The two numbers are surprisingly close to each other—considering the differences in treatment of capital charges and the differences in assumptions with respect to kiln size, the rate

at which kilns are utilized during their initial years of operation, and
the mix of new units and substantial expansions.

Economic efficiency versus regional dispersal

India is attempting to build a democratic socialist society. Under
her structure of government, there is an inherent possibility of conflict between the goals of economic efficiency and of regional dispersal of industry. Large, economical manufacturing units *may* be
incompatible with regional dispersal. In attempting a political
compromise between these conflicting goals, the loss in economic
efficiency is likely to be considerably smaller if a multi-industry
rather than a single-industry viewpoint can be adopted.

Even if one places heavy weight upon the goal of regional dispersal, this does not mean that each decision on plant size has to be
dominated by the doctrine of 'fair shares' for each state. The existing
geographical distribution of resources and markets may by itself
lead to a considerable dispersal of economic opportunities. E.g. in
this chapter we have suggested that large cement plants ought to be
located in Bihar, Rajasthan and Madhya Pradesh (states with limestone deposits adjacent to large markets). According to the preceding chapter, major caustic soda plants ought to be located either
in Maharashtra (the principal market) or in Madras and other low-
cost electricity states.

These results should not be taken to mean that geographical
chance will lead automatically to an acceptable pattern of industrial
location. They do mean, however, that in attempting to arrive at
'fair shares' for the states within a plan period, the individual industry is altogether too narrow a basis for squaring accounts. A more
satisfactory basis would be the *aggregate* volume of investment
allocated to each state.

APPENDIX A

EXPLANATORY NOTE ON THE STATE-WISE DEMAND FOR CEMENT IN 1965-66 AND 1970-71

T. R. TALWAR

A forecast of the state-wise demands for cement during the periods 1965–66 and 1970–71 is presented in Table 6.3. The actual consumption of cement in 1960–61 is also shown in comparison. The demand for cement depends upon the magnitude of investment in different sectors of the economy and in different regions. It has, therefore, been worked out by multiplying the norms of cement consumption together with the investment forecast in different sectors.

The cement consumption norm is defined as the quantity of cement required per million rupees of total investment. The norms have been worked out from primary sources of data and have been discussed in detail in Perspective Planning Division (1962).

The investment programme in the Fourth Plan in turn depends upon the physical output targets for each sector of the economy. The regional distribution of investment in individual sectors of the economy has been calculated under separate assumptions, depending upon the information available in different sectors.

The regional distribution of investment in the industries, mining and power sector has been worked out on the basis of the location of major projects which cover about 80% of the total investment in these sectors. The regional distribution of investment in the transport sector has been assumed proportional to that in industries, mining and power. The distribution of investment in housing has been assumed proportional to the increase in population in the different regions. In the case of health, it has been related to the population not covered by water supply and sanitation facilities. The detailed interim reports prepared by the Working Groups for the formulation of the Fourth Plan form the basis for minor irrigation and education. In the case of small scale industries and agricultural programmes, the Third Plan allocations form the basis of their regional distribution.

REFERENCES

Chatterjee, Pareshnath, *Inter-Firm Comparisons in India*, Delhi University, Delhi, (unpublished manuscript), 1963.

Ghosh, A., *Efficiency in Location and Interregional Flows* (*The Indian Cement Industry during the Five Year Plans 1950–59*). North Holland Press, Amsterdam, 1965.

Healey, J. M., 'An Analysis of Railway Costs and Prices', *The Economic Weekly*, January 1964.

Indian Statistical Institute, *Price Policy for Coal Undertakings*, New Delhi, February 1963.

Joint Technical Group on Transport Planning, *Study of Transportation of Cement in India by Rail and Other Means of Transport*, Planning Commission, New Delhi, May 1963.

Khatau, R. M., 'Cement-making Machinery: A New Industry Forges Ahead', *The Economic Times*, February 1964.

Perspective Planning Division, *Demand for Cement, India 1960–70*, Planning Commission, New Delhi, January 1962.

Perspective Planning Division, *Notes on Perspective of Development, India: 1960–61 to 1975–76*, Planning Commission, New Delhi, April 1964.

Planning Commission, *The Third Plan Mid-term Appraisal*, Government of India, November 1963.

Podder, V., *Cement Industry in India*, Rohtas Industries Limited, Dalmianagar, 1962.

United Nations, *Studies in Economics of Industry, Cement/Nitrogenous Fertilizers Based on Natural Gas*, ST/ECA/75, New York, 1963.

CHAPTER 7

THE NITROGENOUS FERTILIZER INDUSTRY

ALAN S. MANNE

P. N. RADHAKRISHNAN

and

T. V. S. RAMA MOHAN RAO[1]

Summary

This analysis of the nitrogenous fertilizer industry applies both the single- and the two-phase models for multiple producing areas. The chapter begins by outlining the basic data inputs: demand forecasts, product-mix, raw material availability, choice of processes, capital and operating costs of manufacturing and transport costs. Each of these elements required a combination of both judgment and objective facts. On the basis of the data that appeared most reasonable, the model yields the following policy recommendations:

(1) It would be economical to standardize ammonia plants at a single size for single-stream units: 200 thousand tons per year. With the plant size restricted to this one level, the gains from standardization appear to outweigh the costs.

(2) There are economic advantages in concentrating fertilizer production in 200 thousand ton units located at regional petroleum refining centres, and transporting products to the markets in individual states. If, however, there are compelling political reasons to take up the production of fertilizer on a state-by-state basis, then there are significant benefits from time-phasing the projects so that two adjacent states do not construct plants simultaneously.

(3) Unlike the previous results for caustic soda, cement and aluminium, where the present licensing policies result in plant sizes that appear unduly small, the official programme for new plants in the fertilizer industry generally correspond to the sizes indicated by our analysis.

(4) There is a heavy reliance upon the North West refinery (proposed location—Rajasthan) for naphtha feedstock. This assump-

[1] The authors are grateful to B. K. Banerjee, T. N. Srinivasan, and A. Vaidyanathan for their helpful comments and suggestions, and to B. K. Aggarwal for his help with numerical analysis.

tion needs continuing scrutiny if the nitrogenous fertilizer industry is to meet its output targets.

(5) The 'representative points' adopted for each state have not been chosen with sufficient care to insure minimization of *intra*state transport costs of final fertilizers. In order to select the exact plant locations and in order to plan the supply of naphtha from the nearest refinery, it would be essential to calculate these points more accurately.

Demand forecasts

In Perspective Planning Division (1964), it has been estimated that a nitrogen fertilizer equivalent of 1·75 million tons will be demanded in 1970–71. This will be the target adopted here, even though other sources have estimated it at higher levels.

Our best estimate is that actual consumption in 1965–66 will be the equivalent of 0·75 million tons of nitrogen. Of this, 0·50 million tons are expected to come from domestic output, and the rest will be imported. (This is the same ratio between domestic output and imports that prevailed during 1962–63. See Fertiliser Association of India (1963).) By 1970–71, we assume that the utilization rate of domestic capacity will be improved sufficiently so that this additional source of supply will be just sufficient to handle the domestic consumption being satisfied by imports during 1965–66. Thus the total output from new plants to be constructed during the Fourth Five Year Plan is 1·00 million tons of nitrogen.

Based on the fertilizer dose recommendations for various crops in different states and earmarking certain areas to be fertilized, state-by-state forecasts are made in Table 7.1. The area to be fertilized under each crop is determined on the basis of present levels and trends of fertilizer consumption over the past years as well as the magnitude of the overall fertilizer target. Due account has been taken of the priority of irrigated and rainfed areas to be covered by the fertilizer programme. The fertilizer requirements for plantation crops have been allocated to states. E.g. all tea has been put under Assam. Coffee has been apportioned between Kerala and Madras in the ratio 1:2, and rubber is assigned entirely to Kerala.

Choice of solid fertilizers and product-mix

There are a variety of solid nitrogenous fertilizers which deserve consideration depending on the soil conditions, water logging in cropped fields and the ease with which the fertilizer can be applied. A judicious choice of the specific products to be produced in a state will

TABLE 7.1

Projected demands for nitrogenous fertilizers by states
(all figures in thousand metric tons)

	Equivalent nitrogen				Equivalent ammonia, annual increase*
	1965–66	1970–71	Increase over Fourth Plan	Annual increase	
South East	*290·6*	*404·5*	*113·9*	*22·78*	*29·72*
Andhra Pradesh	155·8	227·3	71·5	14·30	18·65
Madras	134·8	177·2	42·4	8·48	11·07
South West	*82·9*	*191·7*	*108·8*	*21·76*	*28·39*
Mysore	44·2	120·0	75·8	15·16	19·78
Kerala	38·7	71·7	33·0	6·60	8·61
East	*70·7*	*196·8*	*126·1*	*25·22*	*32·90*
Assam	36·0	61·8	25·8	5·16	6·73
West Bengal	24·0	89·0	65·0	13·00	16·96
Orissa	10·7	46·0	35·3	7·06	9·21
North East	*126·2*	*378·8*	*252·6*	*50·52*	*65·91*
Bihar	42·4	113·8	71·4	14·28	18·63
Uttar Pradesh—					
East	50·3	159·0	108·7	21·74	28·37
West	33·5	106·0	72·5	14·50	18·91
North West	*68·0*	*223·0*	*155·0*	*31·00*	*40·43*
Punjab, Jammu & Kashmir	57·2	157·0	99·8	19·96	26·03
Rajasthan	10·8	66·0	55·5	11·04	14·40
West Central	*53·7*	*154·3*	*100·6*	*20·12*	*26·24*
Gujarat	26·4	84·1	57·7	11·54	15·05
Madhya Pradesh	27·3	70·2	42·9	8·58	11·19
Maharashtra	*57·9*	*200·9*	*143·0*	*28·60*	*37·30*
Maharashtra	57·9	200·9	143·0	28·60	37·30
Total, all India	750·0	1,750·0	1,000·0	200·00	260·89

NOTE: * Based on mix of 1·0 tons urea and 1·5 tons ammonium sulphate per ton of ammonia. Nitrogen contents of these products are 46% and 21%, resulting in 0·77 tons of nitrogen per ton of ammonia.

depend on the crop structure and agronomic conditions. The fertilizer recommendations of the Fertiliser Association of India provide the dose in terms of nitrogen and the approximate time at which application is feasible—cropwise—in each state but nothing about the type of fertilizer. Ammonium sulphate is the most widely used fertilizer on various soils and crops. The whole of this product is water soluble, has good storage qualities and is easy to handle. Urea is a more concentrated product than ammonium sulphate, and contains 44–46% of nitrogen per ton. It is likely to be leached out from the soil and should not be applied to soils containing free water. Storage of this product is a problem even if it is available in prilled form. Urea could, however, be employed in northern areas for crops requiring less water, or where kharif and rabi crops are grown under controlled irrigation.

There are specific uses in which it is advantageous to utilize other forms of nitrogenous fertilizer: ammonium chloride, ammonium nitrate, ammonium sulphate-nitrate, ammonium phosphate and aqueous ammonia. Ammonia is an intermediate in producing each of these products, and the value added in the conversion process is lower than the cost of the intermediate. Hence—for purposes of selecting an optimal *ammonia* plant size—it seemed best to study a single mix of finished products. As a mix that might be appropriate under Indian conditions during the Fourth Plan, we have chosen ammonium sulphate and urea. Ammonium sulphate is a traditionally popular fertilizer. However, per ton of nitrogen, urea is less expensive to produce, and also has the advantage of being the least bulky solid product. Whenever transport costs are proportional to bulk, this permits supplying nitrogen at the lowest transport cost to the consumer. Urea is therefore a product which is favourable to large plant sizes for ammonia.

There are 0·60 tons of ammonia required per ton of urea and 0·26 tons per ton of ammonium sulphate. Our typical mix is expressed in terms of the equivalent ammonia: 1 ton of ammonia resulting in 1 ton of urea and 1·5 tons of sulphate as end products in the complex of solid fertilizer.

Initial state of the industry

Table 7.2 indicates the location of existing and proposed fertilizer factories in India as of July 31, 1963. The capacity ranges up to 100 thousand metric tons per year of nitrogen. Nangal, the largest plant in 1963, is based on electrolysis of water and has the highest costs. Several of the existing fertilizer plants are working well below capacity—typically for lack of raw materials or electricity rather than lack of demand.

We cannot be certain of the exact quantity of dispatches for the initial conditions of our model as of 1965–66. It is assumed, however, that with better capacity utilization the 1963 level of imports could be virtually wiped out.[1] As can be seen from the table, a variety of

TABLE 7.2

Location of major nitrogenous fertilizer factories as of July 31, 1963*

Location	Product	Capacity, metric tons per year of nitrogen
In production		
1. Sindri, Bihar	ammonium sulphate	73,260
2. Alwaye, Kerala	ammonium sulphate	20,930
3. Sindri, Bihar	ammonium sulphate-nitrate	36,450
4. Rourkela, Orissa	calcium ammonium-nitrate	60,880
5. Nangal, Punjab	calcium ammonium-nitrate	82,480
Licensed and yet to go into production		
6. Namrup, Assam	ammonium sulphate	20,600
7. Alwaye, Kerala	ammonium sulphate	20,930
8. Hanumangarh, Rajasthan	ammonium sulphate	81,580
9. Rourkela, Orissa	calcium ammonium-nitrate	60,880
10. Kothagudem, Andhra Pradesh	urea	80,470
11. Namrup, Assam	urea	24,200
12. Baroda, Gujarat	urea	40,640
13. Neyveli, Madras	urea	71,120
14. Trombay, Maharashtra	urea	45,000
15. Gorakhpur, Uttar Pradesh	urea	80,470
16. Durgapur, West Bengal	urea	59,010
Planned and yet to be licensed†		
17. Mangalore, Mysore	ammonium sulphate	30,000
18. Korba, Madhya Pradesh	urea	100,000
19. Mangalore, Mysore	urea	40,000

* *Source:* Fertiliser Association (1963).

Major plant denotes 20,000 tons/year or more. Other small plants are not listed. Complex fertilizers are also not listed here.

† Provisional.

[1] Otherwise we would have to allow for continuous imports of at least 250,000 tons, or would have to provide additional capacity in the Fourth Plan to catch up with this backlog of internal demand.

nitrogenous fertilizers are being produced and planned: ammonium sulphate, ammonium sulphate-nitrate, urea, calcium ammonium-nitrate, etc. As of 1963, the factories located in Bihar, Orissa, Madhya Pradesh and some in Uttar Pradesh were operating on coal, and only a small quantity of output was based on naphtha. For the Fourth Plan, the trend is towards the naphtha-based process since as will be seen later, it is less expensive than coal.

Raw material availability

For ammonia manufacture, the cheapest raw material available is natural gas.[1] Natural gas has been found in Naharkatiya in Assam, and explorations are progressing in Rajasthan and Punjab. We did not study this aspect in detail since the Assam region has a low demand for fertilizer and could be supplied either through natural gas or through the surplus naphtha available there.

Many of the existing plants are coal-based, but the cost and availability of coal as specified in Indian Statistical Institute (1963) suggests that there is hardly any justification for coal-based fertilizer plants except in Bihar and Madhya Pradesh. Even in these regions, as will be seen below, other cost factors are unfavourable to coal.

Naphtha (boiling point 150–350°F.) is obtained as a joint product in the fractional distillation of crude oil. It is used primarily as a component of motor spirit. Therefore the availability of naptha will depend on the demand for motor spirit, and the regional patterns of its availability can readily be altered by a change in refinery blending and distribution practices. Table 7.3 gives a tentative picture of the availability of naphtha after making allowance for motor spirit and petrochemicals. Note that in seven of the eight refinery areas, there would be enough surplus naphtha available to serve as feedstock for a 200 thousand tons per year ammonia plant.

Choice of process, capital and operating costs, economies-of-scale

Here we discuss the cost of naphtha versus coal as alternative raw materials for ammonia production. (Natural gas steam reforming is less capital-intensive, but the reasons for not considering it have already been indicated in the section on raw material availability.) The costs of ammonia production are likely to be 50% or more of the total costs in a fertilizer plant, and it is therefore essential to select a minimum-cost process for this intermediate. The following are estimates of capital costs for a 100 thousand tons per year ammonia

---

[1] Other raw materials such as coke oven gas or refinery gas are by-products available from other processes and could conceivably be cheaper in some situations. These are neglected here.

TABLE 7.3

Availability of naphtha by states in 1970–71
(thousand tons per year)

	Year	Avail- ability of naphtha	For motor spirit and petro- chemicals	Net available for other uses§
1. Koyali Refinery, Gujarat	1966–67	620	241	379
	1970–71	840	602	238
2. North West Refinery, Rajasthan*	1970–71	400	168	232
3. Cochin Refinery, Kerala	1966–67	375	87	288
	1970–71	373	108	265
4. Bombay Refineries, Maharashtra	1966–67	961	302	659
	1970–71	992	683	309
5. Madras Refinery, Madras†	1970–71	400	207	193
6. Vizag Refinery, Andhra Pradesh	1966–67	186	42	144
	1970–71	346	53	293
7. Assam and Bihar Refineries	1966–67	740	322	418
	1970–71	732	272	460
8. Haldia Refinery, West Bengal‡	1970–71	507	350	157
9. Total	1970–71	4,590	2,443	2,147

* Likely to come on stream in 1969.
† Likely to come on stream in 1967.
‡ Likely to come on stream in 1968.
§ Perspective Planning Division (1964) provides for $1 \cdot 0$ million tons of naphtha for fertilizers in 1970–71 and $2 \cdot 0$ million tons in 1975–76.

plant based on three alternative process and raw material combinations:

naphtha–steam reforming — $54 \cdot 00 \ 10^6$ Rs.
naphtha–partial oxidation — $67 \cdot 20 \ 10^6$ Rs.
coal–partial oxidation   — $92 \cdot 93 \ 10^6$ Rs.

The costs for the steam reforming process in India are obtained by inflating the US costs of erected plants by 40%, as suggested in an unpublished petrochemicals report by the Institut Français du Pétrole. The other estimates are from Indian project records.

When a ton of naphtha is assumed to cost Rs. 85[1] and coal (10,000 BTU/lb.) is valued at Rs. 23 per ton, operating costs (proportional to output) per ton of ammonia by the above processes are respectively Rs. 160·48, 204·76 and 213·58. More details are given in Tables 7.4 and 7.5. The cost structure there suggests that it is considerably cheaper to adopt the naphtha–steam reforming process.[2]

Ammonia is made by combining nitrogen and hydrogen. (The carbon dioxide available as a by-product in the manufacture of ammonia is sufficient to convert the entire ammonia into urea by the total recycle process.) Nitrogen is obtained from air either by distillation of liquid air or by removal of oxygen through a combustion process. The main cost saving can be seen through the following chemical reactions:

Steam reforming: hydrocarbon + steam + air →
                   hydrogen + nitrogen + carbon monoxide

Partial oxidation: hydrocarbon + oxygen + steam →
                     hydrogen + carbon monoxide

The steam reforming process results in a mixture of hydrogen and nitrogen which can be combined in a 3:1 ratio to produce ammonia. The partial oxidation process requires a separate liquid air distillation unit as a source of nitrogen. Until recently, partial oxidation has been favoured because of its flexibility. This process makes it possible to shift from one raw material to another in the same plant. But, after the most recent developments in the steam reforming process for naphtha, the partial oxidation process seems definitely disadvantageous. For these reasons, our plant size analysis is confined to the steam reforming process.

Information on investment costs was available for US erected plants of various sizes for the steam reforming of naphtha.[3] The range of sizes covered is 50,000 tons to 200,000 tons per year of ammonia

[1] Under the naphtha surplus conditions prevailing in India, the price of naphtha is governed primarily by its fuel oil replacement value. Hence, instead of a uniform refinery price for naphtha, it might also be worth considering a price structure based on the fuel substitution possibilities between coal and petroleum products. This would entail a higher price for naphtha in the coal deficit areas located at long distances from Bihar and West Bengal.

[2] For a detailed discussion of production costs of ammonia by various processes other than steam reforming of naphtha, see Viswanathan and Mukherjee (1963).

[3] This information was very kindly provided to us by Mr. Taki Rifai of the Institut Français du Pétrole.

TABLE 7.4a

Operating costs proportional to output
(Rs. per ton of ammonia)

Inputs	Price per unit (Rs.)	Naphtha-steam reforming		Naphtha-partial oxidation		Coal-partial oxidation	
		qty.	cost	qty.	cost	qty.	cost
Naphtha	85/ton	0·825	70·13	0·825	70·13	—	—
Coal (10,000 BTU/lb.)	23/ton	—	—	—	—	2·05	47·15
Power	0·06/kwh.	720	43·20	1,460	87·60	1,930	115·80
Steam	15 and 8·4/ton	—	—	2	30·00	4	33·60
Process water	0·25/10³ gal.	75	18·75	6·660	1·67	6·660	1·67
Boiler feed water	1·00/10³ gal.	1·40	1·40	0·36	0·36	0·36	0·36
Chemicals and supplies		—	12·00	—	—	—	—
Labour and Supervision		—	15·00	—	15·00	—	15·00
Total (Rs./ton)		—	160·48	—	204·76	—	213·58

Sources: For steam reforming process—J. Voogd and J. Tielrooy (1963). For other processes—Indian project reports.

TABLE 7.4b

Operating costs proportional to output
(Rs. per ton of product)

Inputs	Price per unit (Rs.)	Urea by total liquid re-cycle process*		Sulphuric acid by contact process		Ammonium sulphate by acid process	
		qty.	cost	qty.	cost	qty.	cost
Ammonia	160·48/ton†	0·60	96·29	—	—	0·26	41·72
Sulphur	185/ton	—	—	0·35	64·75	—	—
Sulphuric acid	78·90/ton	—	—	—	—	0·80	63·12
Power	0·06/kwh.	250	15·00	60	3·60	90	5·40
Process water	0·25/10³ gal.	5·5	1·37	1·5	0·38	4·5	1·13
Boiler feed water	1·00/10³ gal.	—	—	0·17	0·17	—	—
Chemicals and supplies		—	2·00	—	—	—	—
Labour and supervision		—	8·00	—	10·00	—	16·00
Total (Rs./ton)		—	122·66	—	78·90	—	127·37

NOTES: * Carbon dioxide will be available free of cost from ammonia plant.
    † Proportional operating costs only, carried forward from Table 4a.

Source: Indian project reports.

TABLE 7.5

Investment costs of standard size plants (Rs. millions present worth, discounting in perpetuity at 10% per annum)

	ammonia (naphtha-steam reforming)	ammonia (coal-partial oxidation)	urea-ammonium sulphate (including ammonia from naphtha-steam reforming)
Size (10^3 tons/yr.)	100 ammonia	100 ammonia	100 urea 150 sulphate
1. Initial investment once for all time	54·00	92·93	109·12
2. Replacement of initial investment every 24 years*	5·40	9·29	10·91
3. Maintenance and overheads, 6% of item (1) per year in perpetuity	32·40	55·76	65·50
4. Total present value (10^6 Rs.)	91·80	157·98	185·53
Economies-of-scale parameter	0·79	0·63	0·73

Sources: For steam reforming process—J. Voogd and J. Tielrooy (1963). For other processes—Indian project reports.

* With a plant life of 24 years and a 10% per year discount rate, the replacement factor ρ turns out to be 1·10. (See equation (2.6).) From the viewpoint of a private investor, this 24-year service life for a fertilizer plant would almost surely be regarded as excessive. The private investor would base his calculations upon a shorter service life, e.g. 10 years. With a 10-year service life and a 10% discount rate, the replacement factor would then be raised from 1·10 to 1·58. This would have the direct effect of raising the calculated cost of producing fertilizer. It would, however, have the indirect effect of making it more desirable to economize upon the initial outlays for plant investment rather than upon the current outlays for transportation. That is, a lower service life would make it even more attractive to build large fertilizer plants than is indicated in Table 7.8.

for single-stream plants. Within this size range, the scaling factor is 0·79.[1]

On the basis of the available investment costs for urea and ammonium sulphate plants,[2] the scaling factor for an integrated naphtha-based nitrogenous fertilizer complex is taken to be 0·73. Using this scaling factor together with the investment costs for the standard size plant shown in Table 7.5, we have extrapolated to obtain the investment costs at all other levels of capacity. One qualification: For ammonia plants beyond 200,000 tons per year in capacity, it is believed that the incremental investment costs would continue to decline. In order to err on the conservative side, we have assumed that the incremental investment costs for these large plants will remain constant at the same level as estimated for a 200,000 ton plant.

A further comparison of investment costs for coal versus naphtha processes

In terms of operating costs, it has already been noted that naphtha has an advantage of Rs. 54 per ton of ammonia as against coal (Rs. 160 versus 214). In this section we compare the ammonia investment costs associated with these two raw materials, taking due account of the differences in economies-of-scale. The costs of future installations are calculated using a continuously compounded discount rate of 10% per year. Capacity costs are based upon those shown in Table 7.5 for a single standard installation; i.e. they already include an allowance for the initial installation, replacement every 24 years, and maintenance and overheads at 6% per year on the initial investment. For plant sizes other than the standard ones shown in Table 7.5, an economies-of-scale factor of 0·79 is applied for naphtha-based plants and one of 0·63 for coal.

The capacity costs shown hereafter refer to the series of future installations required in order to satisfy the constantly growing demand over an infinite horizon. With a discount rate of 10% and scaling factors of 0·79 and 0·63, the optimal cycle times are 4·5 and 8·5 years respectively between successive ammonia installations in a single region. Table 7.6 expresses the investment costs in two ways: (*a*) the present value of the rupees expended over an infinite horizon, using the optimal cycle time between installations, and (*b*) the

---

[1] The scaling factor varies from 0·63 for coal-partial oxidation (the most capital intensive) to 0·88 for steam reforming-natural gas (the least capital intensive).

[2] These are available in United Nations (1963), and show good agreement with Indian project reports.

I

TABLE 7.6

Investment cost comparisons between coal and naphtha processes for ammonia; single-phase cycles; discounting at 10% per year

	Annual increase in demand (thousand tons per year of ammonia)	Optimal plant size (thousand tons per year of ammonia)		Investment costs, present value over infinite horizon (Rs. millions)		Investment costs, equivalent Rs. per ton of future demand and output; see equation (6.2)	
		Naphtha-based; 4·5 year cycles	Coal-based; 8·5 year cycles	Naphtha-based	Coal-based	Naphtha-based	Coal-based
South East							
Andhra Pradesh	18·7	85		222·8		119	
Madras	11·1	50		146·5		132	
South West							
Mysore	19·8	90	170	233·1	387·6	118	196
Kerala	8·6	40		122·8		143	
East							
Assam	6·7	30		97·9		146	
West Bengal	17·0	80		212·4		125	
Orissa	9·2	42		127·7		139	
North East							
Bihar	18·6	85		222·8		120	
Uttar Pradesh,							
East	28·3	128	244	306·5	489·3	109	173
West	18·9	85	163	222·8	378·3	118	200
North West							
Punjab, Jammu & Kashmir	26·0	117	224	286·0	462·2	110	178
Rajasthan	14·4	65		180·3		125	
West Central							
Gujarat	15·1	68		186·8		124	
Madhya Pradesh	11·2	50	96	146·5	270·6	131	242
Maharashtra							
Maharashtra	37·3	168		381·7		103	

equivalent cost of this capacity per ton of future demand and output (see equation (6.2).)

Table 7.6 makes comparisons of investment costs—assuming that after 1965–55 each of the 15 states will be self-sufficient with respect to increases in ammonia demand.[1] Even with this decentralized pattern of production, it is clear that naphtha-based plants would be less expensive than coal. The investment cost saving ranges from Rs. 64/ton of ammonia in Uttar Pradesh, East, up to Rs. 111 in Madhya Pradesh. These amounts, when combined with the operating cost saving of Rs. 54/ton, would far outweigh the cost of transporting naphtha into the coal-producing states that have no refineries. Hereafter, our analysis assumes that all new nitrogenous fertilizer plants will be based upon naphtha.

Transport costs

In order to proceed with the evaluation of alternatives, we now introduce estimates of transport costs. The rates shown in Table 7.7 are applicable to rail shipments by wagon loads. To these are added a 5% surcharge to arrive at the actual rates charged during 1964. The rail distances between representative points are the standard ones shown in Table 4.2.

In the caustic soda report (Chapter 5), Appendix B referred to the controversy over the telescoping pattern of the tariff structure—the increment in rate per unit increment in distance. It appears inappropriate to review this controversy again here.

Just as excessive telescoping leads to a bias in favour of a small number of large plants located at long distances from their markets, so also does a rate structure that artificially permits the shipment of finished fertilizers (urea and ammonium sulphate) at much lower rates per ton of bulk than for the raw materials, naphtha and ammonia. (See Table 7.7.) For want of a better alternative, we shall assume that the 1964 rate structure is a rational one based upon the long-run marginal costs of the railways. This assumption is exceedingly dubious. It is quite likely that the rail rates discriminate unduly against the transport of 'dangerous petroleum products'. The discriminatory aspect of the rate structure will surely come under closer scrutiny at a future time when India begins to plan pipelines for the transport of refined petroleum products as well as for crude oil.

[1] Note that Uttar Pradesh is divided into two parts, with Kanpur as the representative point in the East and Delhi in the West. The Jammu and Kashmir demands are consolidated with those of the Punjab. Nagaland, Manipur and Tripura demands are consolidated with those of Assam.

TABLE 7.7

Railway freight rates, wagon loads

	Rs. per metric ton of bulk			
Kilometres	Naphtha	Ammonia	Ammonium sulphate	Urea* (for agricultural use only)
1– 70	14·10	15·30	6·00	7·20
71– 150	23·70	25·70	9·10	11·00
151– 200	29·30	31·80	10·70	12·90
201– 250	34·80	37·80	12·20	14·80
251– 300	40·10	43·60	13·60	16·50
301– 350	45·30	49·40	15·00	18·30
351– 400	50·60	55·10	16·40	20·00
401– 450	55·90	60·90	17·90	21·80
451– 500	61·00	66·40	19·20	23·40
501– 550	65·60	71·40	20·30	24·80
551– 600	70·30	76·60	21·50	26·30
601– 650	75·10	81·90	22·70	27·80
651– 700	79·90	87·00	23·90	29·20
701– 750	84·70	92·30	25·10	30·70
751– 800	89·40	97·50	26·40	32·20
801– 850	93·40	101·80	27·40	33·40
851– 900	97·30	106·00	28·40	34·70
901– 950	101·10	110·20	29·30	35·90
951–1,000	105·00	114·40	30·30	37·10
1,001–1,100	112·50	122·70	32·30	39·60
1,101–1,200	120·20	131·10	34·30	42·00
1,201–1,300	127·80	139·40	36·30	44·40
1,301–1,400	134·90	147·00	38·00	46·50
1,401–1,500	141·90	154·70	39·70	48·60
1,501–1,600	148·80	162·30	41·40	50·70
1,601–1,700	155·90	170·00	43·10	52·80
1,701–1,800	162·80	177·50	44·80	54·90
1,801–1,900	169·90	185·20	46·50	57·00
1,901–2,000	175·70	191·60	48·00	58·80
2,001–2,100	180·00	196·20	49·10	60·20
2,101–2,200	185·30	202·00	50·60	62·00
2,201–2,300	190·50	207·90	52·00	63·80
2,301 and above	193·20	210·60	52·70	64·60

Source: Indian Railway Conference Association Goods Tariff No. 31A, Part II, Goods Rate Tables in force from 1.7.1962.

NOTE: * This rate is admissible only when the urea is certified 'for agricultural use' by the Ministry of Food.

Before examining the combined effect of transport costs and economies-of-scale in manufacturing, there is one alternative which will be noted briefly and then discarded: the possibility of partial integration between ammonia and fertilizer plants. That is, because of the weight-gaining nature of the process of converting ammonia into fertilizer, it is sometimes desirable to carry on the two steps at two separate locations. In the present case, there are several reasons which led us to omit this possibility. These reasons might well be re-examined if one were to make a more detailed study of the industry:

(1) The inclusion of urea in the product-mix favours an integrated plant. Otherwise, the cost of a urea plant would be increased by the necessity of setting up a separate plant for the manufacture of carbon dioxide—which is available as a free by-product in ammonia production.

(2) It costs more to transport naphtha in the intermediate form of ammonia than in the form of naphtha as such. This will be illustrated at a typical interstate distance: 500 kilometres from a fertilizer plant to its source of naphtha at the nearest refinery. According to Table 7.7, at this distance the transport cost of these alternatives would be as follows:

naphtha as such
$$\text{Rs. } 65 \cdot 60 \text{ per ton naphtha}$$

naphtha in the form of ammonia:

$$\frac{1 \text{ ton ammonia}}{0 \cdot 825 \text{ tons naphtha}} \times \frac{\text{Rs. } 71 \cdot 40}{\text{ton ammonia}} = \frac{\text{Rs. } 86 \cdot 50}{\text{per ton naphtha}}$$

Cost comparisons, single-phase and two-phase cycles

Table 7.8 summarizes the costs of three alternative patterns of time-phasing and location. The locational patterns are based upon a grouping of the states into seven regions—each with a regional centre containing an oil refinery. In all cases the cycle time is held constant at $6 \cdot 0$ years' worth of growth in demand, an interval which is optimal for single-phase cycles with a discount rate of 10% and an economies-of-scale parameter of $0 \cdot 73$ for the ammonia, urea and ammonium sulphate complex. The three alternate cases are distinguished as follows:

Case A: Single-phase cycles; each state perpetually supplies itself; plant size $= 6 \cdot 0$ years' worth of demand growth in individual state.

Case B: Single-phase cycles; each regional centre perpetually

TABLE 7.8

Cost comparison for alternative patterns of plant location and time-phasing; cycle time of 6·0 years*
(all figures in Rs. millions of costs discounted at 10% per year)

Region	South-East	South-West	East	North-East	North-West	West-Central	Maharashtra	Total, all India
Regional centre	Madras	Kerala	West Bengal	Bihar	Rajasthan	Gujarat	Maharashtra	
Other states in region	Andhra Pradesh	Mysore	Assam Orissa	Uttar Pradesh, East and West	Punjab, Jammu and Kashmir	Madhya Pradesh	None	
Case A. Single-phase; each state perpetually supplies itself.								
Manufacturing costs†	753	722	894	1,505	936	691	744	6,245
Naphtha transport‡	0	80	41	210	174	66	0	571
Fertilizer transport	0	0	0	0	0	0	0	0
Total, Case A	753	802	935	17,15	1,110	757	744	6,816
Case B. Single-phase; regional centre perpetually supplies all states in its region								
Manufacturing costs†	631	606	682	1,158	786	579	744	5,186
Naphtha transport‡	0	0	0	0	0	0	0	0
Fertilizer transport	139	124	103	304	173	67	0	910
Total, Case B	770	730	785	14,62	959	646	744	6,096
Case C. Two-phase; regional centre alternates with other states in its region								
Manufacturing costs†	664	644	766	1,343	826	601	744	5,588
Naphtha transport†	0	77	38	204	167	59	0	545
Fertilizer transport	7	4	9	9	6	7	0	42
Total, Case C	671	725	813	1,556	999	667	744	6,175

* End products are urea and ammonium sulphate in product tonnage proportions of 1:1·5.
† Includes only those manufacturing costs subject to economies-of-scale. Does *not* include those costs proportional to output and summarized in Table 7.4b: Rs. 122·66 per ton of urea and Rs. 127·37 per ton of ammonium sulphate.
‡ Naphtha transport costs calculated on assumption that Mysore would receive naphtha from Madras; Orissa from West Bengal; Madhya Pradesh from Gujarat; Punjab from Rajasthan; Uttar Pradesh, East from Bihar; and West from Rajasthan.

supplies all states in its region; plant size $= 6 \cdot 0$ years' worth of demand growth in region.

Case C: Two-phase cycles; regional centre alternates in capacity construction with other states in the region; plant size $= 6 \cdot 0$ years' worth of demand growth in individual state.

In Table 7.8, the discounted costs are broken down into three components: manufacturing costs subject to economies-of-scale, transport costs for the naphtha feedstock, and transport costs for the finished fertilizer. Details on computing the manufacturing and product transport costs have already been outlined in Chapters 2 and 4. Appendix A below contains similar details on the naphtha raw material transport costs.

Among the three patterns of time-phasing and location shown in Table 7.8, note that Case A always minimizes the cost of transporting the fertilizer product to the consuming market; that B minimizes both the costs of manufacturing and also the costs of transporting naphtha; and that C is an intermediate one in each cost component. Of the three cases, the total discounted costs are minimum for B (Rs. 6,096 millions), and slightly more for C (Rs. 6,175 millions). The total discounted costs for A (Rs. 6,816 millions) work out to be approximately 10% higher than for either cases B or C.

The policy of locating large plants at regional centres (Case B) is desirable not only on the basis of the cost calculations presented in Table 7.8, but also because this policy facilitates the standardization of plant sizes in all regions at 200 thousand tons per year of ammonia. If, however, there are compelling political reasons to take up the production of fertilizer on a state-by-state basis, then there are significant benefits from time-phasing as shown in C. In C, both the sizes and locations of plants are identical with those of Case A. These two differ with respect to time-phasing. Case A possesses an advantage in only one of the three cost components: costs of transporting the final product to the second area to meet its growth in demand during the first phase of each cycle. This minor advantage in fertilizer transport costs is more than offset through: (1) the usual reduction in manufacturing costs from postponing the date of the capacity investment in the second area and (2) the saving on transport of naphtha feedstock during the first phase whenever the first area contains an oil refinery and the second does not.

Costs of plant size standardization
Up to this point, we have neglected the costs and benefits of standardizing the sizes of new fertilizer plants. By standardization, we mean identical single-stream units—specifically excluding multiple-

stream systems of equivalent capacity. The benefits to be derived from standardization may be listed as follows:

(1) Savings in capital costs by ordering several identical units at the same time or by ordering duplicate units even if ordered at different times.

(2) Savings in spare parts inventory.

(3) Facilitates transfer of operating experience from one fertilizer plant to another.

(4) Facilitates the domestic manufacture of equipment.

With these benefits in view, we studied the effect upon costs if plants were restricted to a single standard size: 200 thousand tons per year of ammonia in single-stream plants.[1] To simplify the problems of plant location, time-phasing and product-mix, the benchmark conditions are taken to be those of Case B, Table 7.8; single-phase 6-year cycles, naphtha converted into a mix of urea and ammonium sulphate, and each regional centre perpetually supplying all states in its region.

According to Table 7.9, standardization would entail negligible departures from the cost minimum calculated for the non-standard plants appropriate for each region. The only significant discrepancy occurs within the North-East region, a cost increase of 1·5%. If Table 7.9 is at all representative, it is clear that the benefits outweigh the costs of standardization, and that the 200 thousand ton plant size is a reasonable standard for India. This size coincides with current official thinking for units to be initiated during the Fourth Plan. These units are considerably larger than those licensed and yet to go into production as of 1963.

Costs per ton of nitrogen

For comparison with cost figures cited in other sources,[2] it may be of interest to summarize the results of the model into a single figure: Rs. 712, the equivalent cost per ton of nitrogen demanded and produced. In arriving at this total, we will first convert the results of Case B, Table 7.8 into the corresponding unit cost. This figure

[1] With an on-stream efficiency factor of 330 days per year, the standard size corresponds to 600 tons of ammonia per stream day. This is a popular size for plants currently under construction in the USA.

[2] E.g. in Perspective Planning Division (1964), Table B.3 indicates the ex-factory price of nitrogenous fertilizers as Rs. 1,200 per metric ton of nitrogen. Note that this price is set so as to cover costs of production under unfavourable circumstances: random interruptions due to shortages of raw materials and power, obsolete processes based upon raw materials other than naphtha, and small plants.

TABLE 7.9

Cost comparisons between standard and non-standard plant sizes, single-phase cycles; each region perpetually supplies itself

	Present value of manufacturing costs (Rs. millions discounted at 10% per year)*	
	Costs based on non-standard plants, Table 7.8, Case B	Costs based on standardized 200 thousand ton plants for each region
South-East	631	631
South-West	606	609
East	682	682
North-East	1,158	1,175
North-West	786	787
West Central	579	579
Maharashtra	744	744
Totals	5,186	5,207

NOTE: * Includes only those manufacturing costs subject to economies-of-scale within a complex whose end products are urea and ammonium sulphate.

includes all manufacturing costs subject to economies-of-scale plus the cost of transporting naphtha and fertilizers. It *excludes* the proportional manufacturing costs shown in Table 7.4b above, and also excludes the costs of distributing fertilizer to the farmer from a plant located at the representative point of each state:

$$\begin{matrix}\text{Ex-factory cost} \\ \text{per ton of} \\ \text{nitrogen demand} \\ \text{and production;} \\ \text{excludes pro-} \\ \text{portional manu-} \\ \text{facturing costs}\end{matrix} = \frac{\begin{matrix}\text{discounted costs,} \\ \text{Case B, Table 7.8}\end{matrix}}{\begin{matrix}\text{discounted tons of} \\ \text{nitrogen demanded} \\ \text{and produced; see} \\ \text{equation (6.2)}\end{matrix}} = \frac{\text{Rs. 6,096 millions}}{0.2 \text{ million tons}/(0.10)^2}$$

$$= \text{Rs. 305 per ton nitrogen}$$

In Table 7.10, the proportional operating costs per ton of bulk product are converted into the costs per ton of nitrogen, assuming that a representative mix would consist of urea and ammonium sulphate. With the proportional costs at Rs. 407, the total ex-factory costs become Rs. 712 per ton of nitrogen = 305 + 407.

TABLE 7.10

Operating costs proportional to output;
product-mix of urea and ammonium sulphate

		Tons nitrogen		Operating costs proportional to output		
	Product tons per ton of ammonia	per ton of product	per ton of ammonia	per ton of product; from Table 7.4b	per ton of ammonia	per ton of nitrogen
Urea	1·0	0·46	0·46	Rs. 123	Rs. 123	
Ammonium sulphate	1·5	0·21	0·31	127	190	
Total	2·5 tons		0·77 tons		Rs. 313	Rs. 407

APPENDIX A

Raw material transport costs in two-phase cycles[1]

Consider two areas 1 and 2, where the first area has a naphtha surplus and the second a deficit in this raw material. Suppose that a fertilizer plant is constructed in area 1 at the beginning of the first phase of each cycle, and one is built in area 2 at the beginning of the second phase. There is a penalty for transport of the finished product from area 1 to 2 during the first phase, and the penalty function $F(r,y)$ is tabulated in Table 4.1.

We now have to evolve an expression for the transport of raw material to area 2. It will be convenient to use the following symbols:

[1] This problem also arose in connection with chapter 6, 'The Cement Industry'. No details were given there on calculating transport costs for the raw material, coal.

D_j = annual increment in demand in area j ($j = 1, 2$)
x = time interval between successive plants in a given area
y = $xD_1/(D_1 + D_2)$
t = any arbitrary point in time
r = annual discount rate, compounded continuously
c = cost of raw material transport per unit of output of end product

If it were not for the temporary saving on transport of naphtha into area 2 during the first phase of each cycle, we could write the discounted costs of raw material transport over the infinite horizon as follows:

Discounted costs, excluding temporary saving

$$= c \int_{t=0}^{\infty} tD_2 e^{-rt} dt = \frac{cD_2}{r^2}$$

During the first phase of each cycle until time y, there is a temporary saving in naphtha transport. Summing these savings over all future cycles of length x, as in equation (4.3):

Discounted value of transport saving

$$= \frac{c \int_{t=0}^{y} tD_2 e^{-rt} dt}{1 - e^{-rx}} = \frac{cD_2[F(r, y)]}{1 - e^{-rx}}$$

Combining terms, we have the desired result:

Discounted costs of raw material transport

$$= cD_2 \left[\frac{1}{r^2} - \frac{F(r, y)}{1 - e^{-rx}} \right]$$

REFERENCES[1]

Fertiliser Association of India, *Fertiliser Statistics*, 1962–63, New Delhi, 1963.

Indian Statistical Institute, *Price Policy for Coal Undertakings*, New Delhi, 1963.

Perspective Planning Division, *Notes on Perspective of Development—India 1960–61 to 1975–76*, Planning Commission, New Delhi, 1964.

United Nations, *Studies in Economics of Industry, Cement/Nitrogenous Fertilizers Based on Natural Gas*, ST/ECA/75, New York, 1963.

[1] In addition to those references listed here, we have consulted a number of project reports and other unpublished materials on the fertilizer industry.

United Nations' Economic Commission for Latin America, *La Industria Química en América Latina*, E/CN.12/628/Add. 3, November 1962.

Viswanathan and Mukherjee, 'Analysis of Possible Investment and Production Costs for Alternative Schemes for Production of Ammonia', United Nations Economic Commission for Asia and Far East, Committee on Industry and Natural Resources, F.1/77, November 1963.

Voogd, J., and J. Tielrooy, 'Make Hydrogen by Naphtha Reforming', *Petroleum Refiner*, March 1963.

CHAPTER 8

CONCLUSIONS ON PLANT SIZE IN INDIA

ALAN S. MANNE

Summary

In three of the four industries studied, there is a substantial discrepancy between the plant sizes and costs that emerge from our model and the actual proposals being considered for the Fourth Plan. It is difficult to believe that the actual proposals could have emerged from any coordinated process for deliberate optimization of plant size, location and time-phasing. Instead, these proposals are results that might be anticipated from a political bargaining process together with piecemeal decision-making.

Results for the three industries are summarized in Table 8.1. (In order to isolate the effects of plant size, this table is based upon the single-phase cycle model, and it excludes proportional manufacturing costs.) Table 8.1 suggests that the difference in those costs affected by plant size optimization might range up to 20%.

If our calculations are correct, India does not suffer universally from *gigantismo*, a malady alleged to be endemic within Latin American economies. In none of the four cases do these calculations suggest a plant size lower than the Fourth Plan proposals. Nitrogenous fertilizers, the one instance where the results coincide with Fourth Plan proposals, also happens to be the only one of these four cases where there have been extensive preinvestment analyses from an industry-wide viewpoint.[1] What is being suggested is *not* that the Indian economy's plant sizes are universally smaller than a techno-economic optimum, but rather that there is a tendency in this direction in the absence of conscious and deliberate benefit-cost calculations.

There are many hypotheses which could account for an apparent tendency towards small plants in India. Some of these hypotheses would operate directly through omissions and biases in our cost minimization model. Other considerations—perhaps more significant ones—are those which stem from the fact that India's planning

---

[1] There have also been industry-wide preinvestment analyses of iron and steel, petrochemicals, and petroleum refining. On the basis of some crude calculations with data for those sectors, our model's results check with the Fourth Plan proposals.

TABLE 8.1

Alternate plant sizes in three industries

	Plant size (thousand tons/year)		Discounted costs affected by plant size optimization		
			(Rs./ton of demand)		Percentage cost difference
	Fourth Plan proposals	Alternative size recommendation	Fourth Plan proposals	Alternative size recommendation	
Aluminium	30	150	Rs. 730*	Rs. 580*	20%
Caustic soda	2–35†	50–150‡	278†	227‡	18%
Cement	200§	400§	37·0§	31·6§	15%

NOTES: * Source: Figure 3.2; excludes proportional manufacturing costs of Rs. 1,720/ton.

† *Source:* Tables 5.2 and 5.6; single-phase, two-year cycles, state market areas; discounted costs equivalent to Rs. 1,626 millions over an infinite time horizon.

‡ *Source:* Tables 5.2 and 5.6; single-phase, five-year cycles, regional market areas; discounted costs equivalent to Rs. 1,329 millions over an infinite time horizon.

§ *Source:* Table 6.4; includes only those elements of manufacturing costs subject to economies-of-scale; discounted costs equivalent to Rs. 6,418 and 5,478 millions over an infinite time horizon.

process is not a monolithic single-person optimization, but instead a multi-person game between the central authorities and the individual enterprises. Some of the flavour of this problem is conveyed in Figure 8.1. Also note the following summary of observations on the Indian economy made by a World Bank mission:

'In many industries, the levels of production are too low to permit full advantage to be taken of the economies-of-scale; this problem is further accentuated by the current policy of giving preference to small and medium-sized units over large ones. . . . Balanced regional development often impedes the growth of the economy as a whole since it detracts from concentration on projects and areas yielding highest economic returns. Industrial management suffers from inefficiencies because it is only gradually being realized that it is a

You Said It

By LAXMAN

I had to adjust, sir. You stated that shortage of funds should not be an excuse for not completing a project!

Reprinted by permission of "Times of India" and R. K. Laxman

Figure 8.1

professional job requiring special experience and expertise. This is particularly true of the public sector; the way in which industry is controlled is of greater significance than the way in which it is owned.'[1]

Some considerations omitted from the cost minimization models

In our calculations, there were a number of simplifications which could have unduly biased the results in favour of large-scale manufacturing units. Perhaps the most serious of these simplifications is the question of technological progress. By supposing that the cost

[1] Cited by Dadachanji (1963).

functions remain stationary over the indefinite future, we have implicitly assumed that the cost-lowering effects of improved technology will be exactly offset by gradual increases in wage costs for construction and equipment manufacture.

If it is anticipated that technological progress will more than offset the rise in construction wage costs, this factor can be incorporated within the model by an increase in the effective rate at which future plant investment costs are discounted. According to Figure 2.4, the higher the discount rate the smaller the optimal plant size. Hence, by ignoring technological progress, it is possible that our numerical calculations have overstated the optimal plant size.

Now if it were true that technological progress is the principal source of bias in our plant size optimization, the model's results should have been farthest away from the Fourth Plan proposals in the case of nitrogenous fertilizers (where progress is taking place at a rapid rate) and closest in the three other industries where progress seems to be taking place more slowly. This is just the reverse of what, in fact, has been observed. On the basis of this indirect evidence, we would conclude that the numerical results cannot be explained away solely through omission of a technological progress factor.

Another possible source of upward bias in our plant size recommendations is the consideration that the raw material supply might impose a constraint on the size of unit constructed in a particular location. E.g. a small limestone deposit would be incompatible with a large cement plant. Similarly, the local availability of naphtha feedstock might limit the size of an ammonia plant; bauxite or electric power might limit an aluminium plant. Although local availabilities could affect the size of a specific project, we have not attempted to include this element directly in our industry-wide models. On the basis of rough calculations for each industry, we believe that there are a sufficient number of locations having raw material supplies compatible with the recommended plant sizes. If the assumption on raw materials is incorrect, this fact ought to show up quite rapidly in the evaluation of specific projects and plant locations.

It could turn out that an individual project location would face still another specific limit on plant size—a limit upon the physical dimensions of the machinery being transported to a new site. Example: If the sections of a kiln for a new cement plant were being transported to a remote inland location via conventional road and/or rail transport, there might be inadequate bridge or tunnel clearances. For this reason, a large plant might require some construction techniques that are currently regarded as unconventional in India—

a greater proportion of on-site welding or even helicopter airlift of over-sized parts. Since these unconventional techniques would depend so much upon the specific site, we have not attempted to adjust the cost curves for this possibility.

There is a further disadvantage in large plants which we have not attempted to quantify. Because of random breakdowns in equipment, the reliability of production will increase if a given volume of capacity is incorporated within several small independent pieces of equipment rather than in a single large one. E.g. if an ammonia plant breaks down for unscheduled maintenance 5% of the time and the desired output is an average of 190 thousand tons per year, one might instal a single unit with an onstream capability of 200 thousand tons—or alternatively two independent units each with an onstream capability of 100 thousand tons. The expected output would be the same in both cases. However, the reliability, the fraction of time that at least half the ammonia plant is in commission, would be 95% in the one case and 99·75% in the other. To offset the lack of reliability with the large-sized individual production unit, it might be necessary to allow for additional intermediate storage. We did not consider this additional storage to be a major cost element, and have not allowed explicitly for it.

Not all of our simplifications have biased the results in favour of large-scale manufacturing units. A number have had the reverse effect. For example, we have counted the costs but excluded the benefits of creating excess plant capacities ahead of demand.[1] We have not counted in the advantage that a large centrally-located plant can pool together the random demands originating from a large number of users scattered over space. And we have not counted in any extra benefits from the fact that large plants would economize upon skilled labour and management, some of the scarcest factors of production. Taking the pros and cons together, we do not believe that the typical plant sizes being proposed for India's Fourth Plan are large enough to lead to an overall minimization of costs in the aluminium, caustic soda and cement industries.

Some consequences of multiple decision centres

In order to understand the actual plant sizes proposed for India's Fourth Plan, we will have to reckon that these investment proposals typically originate in multiple decision centres—each unit seeking to

[1] With occasional excess capacity in these industries, it would be possible to satisfy some users who would otherwise receive too low a priority in the rationing and allocation process.

K

promote its own welfare and not necessarily that of the entire nation. The following classification of alternative hypotheses is not drawn up in the spirit of 'tout comprendre, c'est tout pardonner'. Rather, these hypotheses are intended—speculative as they are—to serve as a basis for possible modifications in public policy so that the national viewpoint may be more closely represented in plant size decisions:

Hypothesis 1: *Regional politics* lead to demands for 'fair shares' in the nation's programme of industrial developments.[1] These demands, as handled currently, result in small, high-cost plants. There is ample room for a more imaginative viewpoint on regional development— fair shares in the overall investment budget rather than in each particular industry. States with small local demands for an item need not be barred indefinitely from producing that item. With demands growing over time, the overall investment programme can be planned so that a large, low-cost unit will *eventually* be constructed in the vicinity of each market having an adequate supply of raw materials.

Hypothesis 2: *Discount rates* have a significant effect upon optimal plant size. Because of fragmentation of the capital markets, these rates differ substantially between the private and the public sector of the Indian economy. The standard rate employed in our calculations (10% per annum) probably exceeds that of most public sector enterprises, and falls short of that in most private firms. In order to move in the direction of optimality for the economy as a whole, these wide differences in the cost of capital will have to be narrowed—perhaps through strengthening the private capital markets, perhaps through public development finance corporations.

Hypothesis 3: *Anti-monopoly sentiments* result in political opposition to large manufacturing units.[2] These sentiments appear altogether misplaced—given the degree of governmental intervention that India has adopted. With imports eliminated by foreign exchange licensing, with new domestic capacity limited by investment licensing

---

[1] There is a striking similarity between these effects of regional politics and the problems of economic integration between sovereign countries, e.g. within the Latin American Free Trade Area or within the Central American Common Market. See Balassa (1965).

[2] Most economies-of-scale in production appear to be associated with the individual plant rather than with the enterprise as a whole. Hence large plants do not necessarily imply large monopolistic enterprises. As time passes and as new plants are set up, additional enterprises can be created—just as in the public sector of the Indian steel industry. The first three integrated mills were set up under the common management of Hindustan Steel, Ltd., but the fourth public sector plant at Bokaro is to be under an independent management.

and by shortages of capital goods, and with formal or informal price controls in most industries, it is wishful thinking to suppose that India can simultaneously enjoy the benefits associated with a competitive structure of industry.

Hypothesis 4: *Excess capacity* is more likely to result from large than from small new plants. From an overall viewpoint, it may pay to create this kind of excess capacity—though not from the viewpoint of the established producers themselves. Conceivably the excess capacity could be large enough to stimulate temporary bouts of price competition. A more realistic fear is that the producing enterprises would—in the presence of excess capacity—be in a weaker bargaining position *vis-à-vis* the price control authorities. Given the structure of the Indian economy, the existing producers can hardly be expected to favour the creation of excess capacity or of large, low-cost new plants.

Hypothesis 5: *Demand estimates* of the Planning Commission are often said to contain an upward bias. From the viewpoint of the individual enterprise, this may indeed be a realistic fear. However, with 'indicative' rather than 'imperative' planning, it is altogether possible that if each decentralized enterprise forecaster makes downward adjustments in the Planning Commission's targets, then these less optimistic prophecies will be self-fulfilling. All that has been attempted in this volume is to suggest plant sizes that would be logically compatible with Plan targets—not to derive the targets themselves.

Hypothesis 6: *Civil servants* in the industrial licensing organizations have little time of their own to spare for investigating optimal plant sizes, locations and time-phasing. The key individuals tend to be overworked and under continual pressure of deadlines—popular newspaper cartoons to the contrary notwithstanding. Most administrators have had to learn economics and administration through on-the-job experience rather than through formal academic training. (To many Indians in responsible managerial positions, even the rationale for discounted cash flows is an unfamiliar concept.) It is little wonder that these civil servants find it difficult to resist the political pressures from all sides. Because of the immediate need to accept or reject a specific project proposal, inadequate provision is made for analysing the consequences of the immediate decision in the long-term perspective of a series of future manufacturing facilities. This volume will have served its purpose if it helps to illustrate that hypothesis 6 is becoming obsolete, and that India is beginning to possess both the data and the analytical skills needed to introduce benefit-cost calculations into sectoral planning.

REFERENCES

Balassa, B., *Economic Development and Integration*, Centro de Estudios Monetarios Latinoamericanos, Mexico, 1965.

Dadachanji, C. J., 'The High Cost of Chemicals Manufacture in India', speech delivered at Indian Chemical Manufacturers' Association, Silver Jubilee, Bombay, December 1963.

PART II

SINGLE PRODUCING AREA–
FURTHER RESULTS

CHAPTER 9

GEOMETRIC RATE OF GROWTH OF DEMAND

T. N. SRINIVASAN[1]

Introduction and summary

In Chapter 2, the following single-phase optimization problem is considered. Suppose (i) the demand for a product in a region grows at a constant arithmetic rate over time; (ii) initially there is just enough capacity to meet the demand; (iii) there are economies-of-scale in construction and operation of plant; (iv) all other costs are proportional to output. Then in order to meet demands at each future point in time, what is the optimal sequence of time of construction and size of plant? The criterion for choice is minimizing the sum of discounted costs. It was shown that it is optimal to construct a plant at each point of a sequence of equally spaced points of time, of size equal to the growth in demand during the time interval between any two such time points. This time interval or time cycle is chosen so as to minimize the discounted stream of costs.

In this chapter, we consider the same problems except that demand will be assumed to grow at a constant *geometric* rate over an infinite horizon, and we shall assume that the cost as a function of plant size v is of the special form: kv^a with $0 < a < 1$. It will be shown that it is still optimal to construct a plant at each point of a sequence of equally spaced time points. However, because of the geometric pattern of growth in demand, the size of plant to be constructed at each such time point will not be the same, but will grow exponentially. As in the arithmetic growth problem, the optimal time interval between any two successive plants is chosen so as to minimize the sum of the discounted stream of costs. This optimal time interval will be numerically computed for alternative values of the economies-of-scale parameter assuming 10% growth and discount rates. The value of the sum of the discounted stream of costs using the optimal time interval will be compared with the costs that would result if one used instead the time interval that is optimal for arithmetic growth of demand. For all parameter combinations an upper and a lower bound for the optimal time interval will be given. However, these

[1] The author is indebted to Alan S. Manne for suggesting the problem and for helpful discussions. Thanks are due to T. V. S. Rama Mohan Rao for computational assistance.

bounds do not appear to be sharp enough, so that their derivation and computation are omitted from this paper.

Some numerical results

Let g be the instantaneous, geometric rate of growth of demand. Let $K(0)$ be the initial demand (equals initial capacity). Then the rate of demand at any arbitrary instant t will be $K(0)e^{gt}$. Let us assume that it is optimal to construct plants at equally spaced time points. Let these time points be 0, x, $2x$, $3x$, . . . Now the growth in demand during the interval $(0, x)$ equals the demand at time x minus the initial demand, or in the above notation $K(0)(e^{gx} - 1)$. Let us denote this by $E(x)$. The size of the plant to be constructed at time point nx will equal the growth in demand during the interval $(nx, (n + 1)x)$. It is easily seen that this equals $K(0)e^{g(n+1)x} - K(0)e^{ngx} = E(x)e^{ngx}$. Thus the sequence of plant sizes is $E(x)$, $E(x)e^{gx}$, $E(x)e^{2gx}$, . . . Given that the cost of construction of a plant of size v is kv^a and the discount rate is r, it is clear that the sum $C(x)$ of the discounted stream of construction costs corresponding to the above sequence is

$$C(x) = \sum_{n=0}^{\infty} e^{-nrx} k\{E(x)e^{ngx}\}^a$$

$$= k\{E(x)\}^a \sum_{n=0}^{\infty} e^{-n(r-ag)x}$$

$$= \frac{k\{E(x)\}^a}{1 - e^{-(r-ag)x}} \text{ (assuming r > } ag) \quad . \quad . \quad (9.1)$$

The optimal time interval x^{**} is obtained by minimizing $C(x)$ with respect to x.

The values of x^{**} when a lies in the empirically relevant range of $(0 \cdot 40, 0 \cdot 90)$ and for $r = g = 0 \cdot 10$ are given in column (2) of Table 9.1. The 10% value for the discount rate r is the one being applied throughout this volume. The 10% value for the demand growth rate g is of the same order of magnitude being projected for caustic soda, cement and other heavy industries in India.

Column (3) of Table 9.1 gives the values of x^*, the optimal cycle time for arithmetic growth in demand (also on the basis that $r = 0 \cdot 10$) for comparison with x^{**}. The optimal time cycle for geometric growth is shorter than that for arithmetic growth. Column (4) of Table 9.1 gives the percentage increase in discounted construction costs that would result if we construct plants every x^* units of time instead of every x^{**} units of time. In the cases considered here the increase in costs does not exceed $3 \cdot 16\%$, and is in fact less than 1%

for $a \geqslant 0 \cdot 65$. It is not clear whether these modest increases in costs continue to hold for other values of r and g as well.

TABLE 9.1*

Economies-of-scale parameter a	Optimal cycle time, geometric growth, x^{**}	Optimal cycle time, arithmetic growth, x^*	Percent increase in discounted costs if x^* is used instead of x^{**} in equation (9.1)
(1)	(2)	(3)	(4)
0·40	11·92	16·17	3·16
0·45	10·73	14·28	2·57
0·50	9·62	12·53	2·00
0·55	8·58	10·97	1·57
0·60	7·58	9·47	1·13
0·65	6·61	8·09	0·80
0·70	5·68	6·76	0·52
0·75	4·74	5·51	0·31
0·80	3·82	4·31	0·16
0·85	2·88	3·18	0·08
0·90	1·95	2·09	0·03

* Thanks are due to the Department of Physics, Delhi University for the use of its I.B.M. 1620 computer in these calculations. It was found that hand computation methods did not permit sufficiently accurate evaluation of the cost function (9.1).

The form of the optimal policy

Let us now establish that the optimal policy consists in constructing plants at equally spaced points of time. Given $K(0)$, g, r and a such that $r > ag$, let the optimal sequence of time points at which plants are to be constructed be $(t_n^{**}) = 0, t_1^{**}, t_2^{**}, t_3^{**}, \ldots$ We wish to show that $t_n^{**} = n\, t_1^{**}$ for $n = 2, 3, \ldots$

Lemma

The optimal time sequence is independent of $K(0)$, the initial capacity (equals demand).

Proof:

The size of plant constructed at t_n^{**} is just sufficient to meet the growth in demand during (t_n^{**}, t_{n+1}^{**}). Hence it must be equal to $K(0)(e^{gt_{n+1}^{**}} - e^{gt_n^{**}})$. Given the discount rate r and construction cost function kv^a where v is the size of a single plant, we see that the discounted sum of construction costs associated with the sequence $\{t_n^{**}\} = 0, t_1^{**}, t_2^{**}, \ldots$ is C^{**} given by

$$C^{**} = \sum_{n=0}^{\infty} e^{-rt_n^{**}} k\{K(0)(e^{gt_{n+1}^{**}} - e^{gt_n^{**}})\}^a$$

$$= k\{K(0)\}^a \sum_{n=0}^{\infty} e^{-rt_n^{**}} \{e^{gt_{n+1}^{**}} - e^{gt_n^{**}}\}^a$$

Consider now any other (non-optimal) sequence $\{t_n\} = 0, t_1, t_2, \ldots$ The sum of discounted costs for such a sequence is C given by

$$C = k\{K(0)\}^a \sum_{n=0}^{\infty} e^{-rt_n} \{e^{gt_{n+1}} - e^{gt_n}\}^a$$

Since the sequence $\{t_n^{**}\}$ is optimal, we must have $C^{**} \leqslant C$. But $C^{**} \leqslant C$ if and only if

$$\sum_{n=0}^{\infty} e^{-rt_n^{**}} \{e^{gt_{n+1}^{**}} - e^{gt_n^{**}}\}^a \leqslant \sum_{n=0}^{\infty} e^{-rt_n} \{e^{gt_{n+1}} - e^{gt_n}\}^a$$

This latter inequality does not depend on $K(0)$. Hence if $\{t_n^{**}\}$ is optimal for one value of $K(0)$, then it is optimal for all values $K(0)$. Note that this result depends crucially on the assumption that construction cost is a power function of size of plant.

With this lemma, we are in a position to show that $t_n^{**} = nt_1^{**}$. Now capacity and demand are both equal to $K(0)e^{gt_1^*}$ at the time point t_1^*. If the sequence $\{t_n^{**}\}$ is to be optimal, given $K(0)$, a, g and r for the entire time horizon $(0, \infty)$ it is obvious that the sub-sequence beginning from t_1^{**}, on, i.e. $t_1^{**}, t_2^{**}, t_3^{**}, \ldots$, must be optimal for the same values of a, g and r and a different initial capacity, namely $K(0)e^{gt_1^{**}}$. This must be so since the future beyond t_1^{**} looks exactly the same as the future from time zero except for a multiplicative factor $e^{gt_1^{**}}$. However we proved in the lemma above, that the optimal time sequence does not depend on the initial capacity level. Hence the optimal sequence from t_1^{**} on must be $t_1^{**}, t_1^{**} + t_1^{**}$, $t_1^{**} + t_2^{**}, \ldots$ This means that $t_2^{**} = 2t_1^{**}$; $t_3^{**} = 3t_1^{**}$, etc. In general $t_n^{**} = nt_1^{**}$.

Having established $t_n^{**} = nt_1^{**}$, we see that C^{**}, the optimal discounted costs, must equal:

$$k\{K(0)\}^a \sum_{n=0}^{\infty} e^{-nrt_1^{**}} \{e^{(n+1)gt_1^{**}} - e^{ngt_1^{**}}\}^a$$

$$= \frac{k \{K(0)\}^a \{e^{gt_1^{**}} - 1\}^a}{1 - e^{-(r - ag)t_1^{**}}}$$

Hence t_1^{**} is that value of t which minimizes

$$C(t) = \frac{\{e^{gt} - 1\}^a}{1 - e^{-(r-ag)t}} \cdot k\{K(0)\}^a$$

From now on, we shall denote the optimal cycle time by x^{**}. To repeat, x^{**} minimizes

$$C(x) = \frac{\{e^{gx} - 1\}^a}{1 - e^{-(r-ag)x}} \cdot k \{K(0)\}^a \quad \ldots \quad \text{(9.1)}$$

Minimizing $\log C(x)$ is equivalent to minimizing $C(x)$. Differentiating $\log C(x)$ with respect to x and equating the derivative to zero, we get the following equation for determining x^{**}

$$ag(e^{\,hx^{**}} - 1) = h\,(1 - e^{-gx^{**}}) \quad \ldots \quad \ldots \quad \text{(9.2)}$$

where $h = r - ag > 0$. We shall show that there exists a unique positive x^{**} which satisfies this equation. This unique x^{**} in fact provides a minimum both for $\log C(x)$, and for $C(x)$, as can be verified by examining the sign of second derivative of $\log C(x)$ at x^{**}.

Let $p(x) = ag(e^{hx} - 1)$ and $q(x) = h(1 - e^{-gx})$. Then x^{**} is the positive solution of $p(x^{**}) = q(x^{**})$. It is easily verified that $p(0) = q(0) = 0$, $p(\infty) = \infty$, $q(\infty) = h > 0$. It is also seen that

$$\frac{dp}{dx} > 0, \frac{d^2p}{dx^2} > 0, \frac{dq}{dx} > 0 \text{ and } \frac{d^2q}{dx^2} < 0 \text{ for all } x > 0.$$

Figure 9.1 illustrates the behaviours of $p(x)$ and $q(x)$ for positive x.

There will exist a unique positive solution for x^{**}.

if $\qquad \dfrac{dp}{dx}\bigg]_{x=0} < \dfrac{dq}{dx}\bigg]_{x=0}$.

Now $\qquad \dfrac{dp}{dx}\bigg]_{x=0} = a\,gh$, and $\dfrac{dq}{dx}\bigg]_{t=0} = hg$.

Since, by assumption (otherwise there will be no economies-of-scale) $0 < a < 1$, an unique positive solution for x^{**} exists.

The following results about x^{**} can be established:

(1) $x^{**} < \dfrac{1}{h} \log \left(\dfrac{r}{ag}\right)$

(2) $x^{**} > \dfrac{1}{g} \log \left(\dfrac{h + g}{r}\right)$

(3) $\lim_{g \to 0} x^{**} = x^*$, i.e. as the (geometric) growth rate g approaches zero, the optimal cycle time x^{**} approaches x^*, the optimal cycle time for arithmetic growth in demand.

(4) x^{**} decreases as the discount rate r increases, other parameters remaining constant.

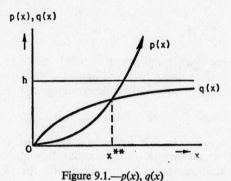

Figure 9.1.—$p(x)$, $q(x)$

CHAPTER 10

OPTIMAL PLANT SIZE WITH TIME-PHASED IMPORTS

DONALD ERLENKOTTER*

This chapter extends the analysis by Manne (1961) of a single producing area problem in which an excess of demand over supply
(demand backlogging) is allowed within the area. The area's deficits
are supplied by unlimited imports at a constant penalty cost per unit.
It is assumed that demand is growing over time at a constant annual
arithmetic rate D and that the discount rate and investment cost
function for constructing plants remain stationary. The plant life
and the time horizon are infinite.

Several of the results obtained are valid for general investment cost
functions. If construction of a plant is ever desirable, the size of the
plant constructed should be at least sufficient to supply any existing
excess demand. The problem then may be reduced to minimization
of a simple expression involving only the single decision variable x,
the number of years of demand growth at the annual rate D that the
plant can supply.

Stronger results and detailed computations are given for the case
in which economies-of-scale in the investment cost for constructing a
plant of size xD are expressed in the form of a power function
$k(xD)^a$, where $0 < a < 1$. It is shown that the optimal plant capacity
increases with decreasing penalty cost. Since an infinite penalty cost
corresponds to the single producing area model with no imports, the
possibility of temporary imports makes larger plants more desirable.
In the no import case, optimal capacity decreases as economies-of-
scale become less pronounced (as the parameter a increases) or as
the discount rate increases. If temporary imports are permitted,
however, the optimal capacity may decrease and then increase as
either a or the discount rate increases.

The plant size model with time-phased imports

Within a single producing area, suppose that the demand for an
industry's product grows at a constant annual arithmetic rate of D
physical units per year over an infinite horizon. Plants may be con-

---

[1] The author is indebted to Alan S. Manne for suggesting the problem and for
helpful discussions.

structed to supply this demand according to an investment cost function $f(xD)$, where xD is the size of plant constructed. The investment cost function is assumed to be stationary over time, and capacity once created is assumed to last indefinitely.

To define a starting-point for the analysis, we look forward from a point in time at which demand has grown to equal the capacity in the area ('regeneration point' as in Manne (1961)). Until the date a new plant goes on stream, demand may be backlogged and satisfied temporarily by imports from an outside source at a penalty cost proportional to the backlogged demand tD at time t. Some plant size decisions may be inferior to a policy of perpetually importing. With unit penalty rate p, a constant discount rate r, and a present value factor of e^{-rt} at time t, an admissible plant size must be such that:

$$f(xD) \leqslant \int_0^\infty (xD)pe^{-rt}dt = (xD)\frac{p}{r} \quad . \quad . \quad . \quad (10.1)$$

If $f(\cdot)$ is such that no value of xD satisfies (10.1), a policy of perpetually importing will be optimal.

Assuming that at least one plant size is admissible, two decisions must be made to minimize the total discounted investment and penalty costs $C(x, y)$: y, the duration of the temporary import phase, and xD, the size of plant to be constructed. It is shown in Appendix A that only policies of the form $y \leqslant x$ need be considered.[1] With $y \leqslant x$, increases in demand eventually exhaust each new increment of capacity, and we are faced again with a situation identical to the initial one. The total discounted costs from a regeneration point are:

$$C(x, y) = \int_0^y p(tD)e^{-rt}dt + e^{-ry}f(xD) + e^{-rx}C(x, y) \quad (10.2)$$

The first term on the right-hand side of (10.2) is the discounted sum of penalty costs during the period before the first plant is constructed, and the second is the present value of the plant investment made in year y. The last term provides the present value of all future costs. From (10.2) we obtain:

[1] The results shown in Appendix A are given for the more general case of non-constant rates of demand growth, i.e. the rate of growth $D(t) \geqslant 0$ is defined over the time index t. The use of these results in the body of this chapter will be restricted to the special case of $D(t) = D$ for all t.

$$C(x, y) = \frac{1}{1 - e^{-rx}}\left\{ p \int_0^y (tD)e^{-rt}dt + e^{-ry}f(xD) \right\}$$

$$= \frac{1}{1 - e^{-rx}}\left\{ \frac{pD}{r^2}[1 - e^{-ry}(1 + ry)] + e^{-ry}f(xD) \right\}$$

$$\tag{10.3}$$

It is also shown in Appendix A that for any admissible plant size xD, the optimal choice of y associated with x satisfies the following expression:

$$y(x) = \frac{rf(xD)}{pD} \leqslant x \quad . \quad . \quad . \quad . \quad (10.4)$$

Substituting this definition for $y(x)$ into (10.3), we may now minimize the following single-variable expression:[1]

$$C(x, y(x)) = \frac{pD}{r^2}\left[\frac{1 - e^{-ry}}{1 - e^{-rx}} \right] \quad . \quad . \quad . \quad (10.5)$$

An equivalent way to measure costs is as the discounted cost per unit demanded. Designating $s(x, y(x))$ as this cost per unit, we have:

$$C(x, y(x)) = \int_0^\infty s(x, y(x))\,(tD)e^{-rt}dt = \frac{D}{r^2} s(x, y(x))$$

Combining this result with (10.5) we obtain

$$s(x, y(x)) = p\left[\frac{1 - e^{-ry}}{1 - e^{-rx}} \right] \quad . \quad . \quad . \quad (10.6)$$

Note that if e^{-ry} is replaced by its series expansion, (10.5) becomes:

$$C(x, y(x)) = \frac{1}{1 - e^{-rx}}\left[f(xD) - \sum_{i=1}^\infty \frac{\left(\frac{r^2}{pD}\right)^i (-f(xD))^{i+1}}{(i + 1)!} \right]$$

Taking the limit as p becomes infinite, we have the cost function for the no-import case:

$$C(x,0) = \frac{f(xD)}{1 - e^{-rx}} \quad . \quad . \quad . \quad . \quad (10.7)$$

---

[1] Numerical minimization of this expression is simple if $C(x, y(x))$ has a unique relative minimum, i.e. $-C(x, y(x))$ is unimodal. The conditions on $f(\cdot)$ which will give this property have not been discovered, although in the following section it is shown for the special case $f(xD) = k(xD)$.[a]

If $f(\cdot)$ is differentiable, a necessary condition for the minimum of (10.5) may be obtained by minimizing log $C(x, y(x))$. Differentiating with respect to x and setting the result equal to zero gives:

$$\frac{d \log C(x, y(x))}{dx} = r\left\{ \frac{rf'(x^*D)}{p(e^{ry^*} - 1)} - \frac{1}{e^{rx^*} - 1} \right\} = 0 \ . \quad (10.8)$$

or,

$$\frac{e^{ry^*} - 1}{e^{rx^*} - 1} = \frac{rf'(x^*D)}{p} = y'(x^*) \quad . \quad . \quad . \quad (10.9)$$

where (x^*, y^*) with $y^* = y(x^*)$ denotes the optimal solution.

The case of $f(xD) = k(xD)^a$—further results

An important specific case, discussed in Chapter 2 above, is the investment cost function

$$f(xD) = k \cdot (xD)^a$$

where we have $k > 0$ and $0 < a < 1$. This investment cost is concave and increasing, providing economies-of-scale which become more pronounced as a becomes smaller. Figure 10.1 graphs the normalized cost function $C(x, y)/kD^a$ for typical values of a, r and the factor kD^a/pD. The use of a logarithmic scale for the capacity increment x shows the approximate symmetry of $C(x, y(x))$ for small proportional changes from x^*. The following properties of the cost function $C(x, y(x))$ may be verified from (10.5):

(i) $\lim\limits_{x \to 0} C(x, y(x)) = +\infty$

(ii) $\lim\limits_{x \to \infty} C(x, y(x)) = \dfrac{pD}{r^2}$

(iii) The unique finite x solution to $C(x, y(x)) = \dfrac{pD}{r^2}$ is obtained at

$$x' = y(x'), \text{ or } x' = \frac{1}{D}\left(\frac{rk}{p}\right)^{1/1-a} .$$

Property (ii) gives the present value of the costs for a policy which satisfies all demand through imports. Property (iii) defines the x' which satisfies (10.1) with equality; a plant size of $x'D$ is the minimum admissible size which is competitive with the imported product.

Since $C(x, y(x))$ is continuous on the interval $(0, + \infty)$, properties (i) and (iii) provide the information that in minimizing $C(x, y(x))$, only values of x on the open interval $(x', + \infty)$ need be considered. It may be shown that on this interval $y(x) < x$. Properties (ii) and (iii) combined with the differentiability of $C(x, y(x))$ on the interval $(x', + \infty)$ indicate that if $C(x, y(x))$ has a zero derivative for a

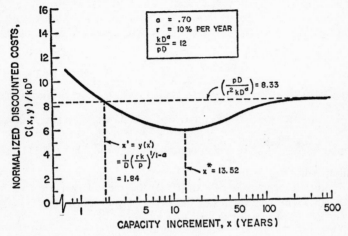

Figure 10.1.—Discounted Cost Function

unique value of x on this interval, this value minimizes the function.

From (10.8), we have the minimizing condition:

$$\frac{d \log C(x, y(x))}{dx} = g(x^*) = \frac{ary^*}{x^* (e^{ry^*} - 1)} - \frac{r}{e^{rx^*} - 1} = 0 \qquad (10.10)$$

or

$$\frac{\dfrac{rx^*}{e^{rx^*} - 1}}{\dfrac{ry^*}{e^{ry^*} - 1}} = \frac{h(x^*)}{h(y^*)} = H(x^*) = a \quad . \quad . \quad . \quad . \quad (10.11)$$

where $h(x) = \dfrac{rx}{e^{rx} - 1}$.

Note that $\lim_{p \to \infty} h(y^*) = \lim_{y \to 0} h(y^*) = 1$. This yields the solution for the no-import case derived in Manne (1961):

L

$$h(x^*) = \frac{rx^*}{e^{rx^*} - 1} = a \quad \cdot \quad \cdot \quad \cdot \quad (10.12)$$

To demonstrate uniqueness of the solution to (10.11), observe first that $h(x)$ is strictly decreasing in x. This shows uniqueness of the solution to (10.12) and, combined with the property that for $x > 0$, $y(x) \gtrless x$ as $x \gtrless x'$, guarantees a unique positive solution to the equation $H(x) = 1$ at $x = x'$. Expression (10.11) will therefore have a unique solution for $0 < a < 1$ if $H(x)$ is strictly decreasing in x for $x \geqslant x'$. Differentiating $\log H(x)$ with respect to x, we have:

$$\frac{d \log H(x)}{dx} = \frac{h'(x)}{h(x)} - \frac{h'(y)}{h(y)}\frac{dy}{dx} < \frac{1}{x}\left[\frac{xh'(x)}{h(x)} - \frac{yh'(y)}{h(y)}\right]$$

since $h(x)$, $h(y)$ are decreasing, and $a < 1$. It may be shown that $\dfrac{xh'(x)}{h(x)}$ is strictly decreasing in x. For $x \geqslant x'$ we have $y(x) \leqslant x$ and hence $\dfrac{d \log H(x)}{dx} < 0$, which completes the proof that (10.11) has a unique solution.

From the properties of $C(x, y(x))$, the second derivative of $\log C(x, y(x))$ with respect to x evaluated at (x^*, y^*) must be positive. A necessary condition for this is:

$$x^* - ay^* \geqslant \frac{1-a}{r}. \quad \cdot \quad \cdot \quad \cdot \quad \cdot \quad (10.13)$$

Verification of (10.13) is left to the reader. In particular, expression (10.13) provides the following lower bound for x^* independent of the penalty cost p:

$$x^* \geqslant \frac{1-a}{r}$$

Parametric study of the model with $f(xD) = k(xD)^a$

Unfortunately, even the simplified expressions (10.5) and (10.11) do not provide the insight into the behaviour of the temporary import model with $f(xD) = k(xD)^a$ that (10.12) provides for the special case of no imports. In the no-import case, optimal values of x^* are readily computed from (10.12) and it is obvious that for fixed values of a, x^* is a decreasing function of r since the product rx^* must be constant. Also, since $h(x)$ is strictly decreasing, x^* is a decreasing function of a, r being held fixed. But for the general case with temporary imports, (10.11) contains factors involving the parameter a

on both sides of the expression. Computation of optimal values must be performed by numerical methods. Tables of calculated results together with a description of the methods used are contained in Appendix B. Selected results from these tables for typical parameter values are presented in Figures 10.2, 10.3 and 10.4.

Figure 10.2 shows the response of the optimal values of x^* and y^* to changes in the penalty factor. The optimal cycle time x^* is an increasing function of the term kD^a/pD. The approximate constancy

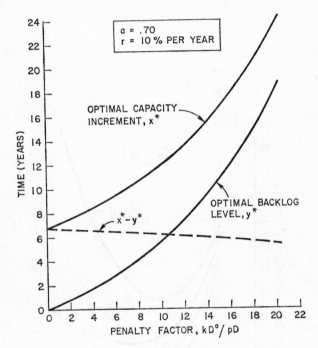

Figure 10.2.—Optimal Solution as Function of Penalty Factor

of the difference $x^* - y^*$ is worthy of note. The response of x^* to variation in p may be shown analytically by using (10.10) as an implicit function relating x^* and p:

$$\frac{\partial x^*}{\partial p} = -\frac{\dfrac{\partial g(x^*)}{\partial p}}{\dfrac{\partial g(x^*)}{\partial x^*}} \qquad \cdots \cdots \quad (10.14)$$

We have

$$\frac{\partial g(x^*)}{\partial p} = \frac{a}{x^*} h'(y^*) \frac{\partial y}{\partial p} > 0$$

since $h(y)$ is decreasing and

$$\frac{\partial y}{\partial p} = -\frac{rk(xD)^a}{p^2 D} < 0$$

Also,

$$\frac{\partial g(x^*)}{\partial x^*} = \frac{d^2 \log f(x^*, y^*)}{dx^2} > 0$$

Hence in (10.14)

$$\frac{\partial x^*}{\partial p} < 0$$

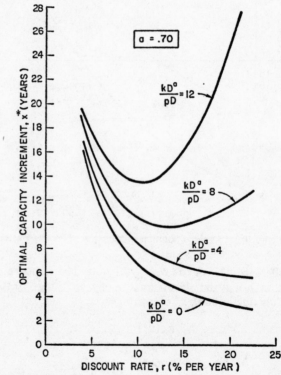

Figure 10.3.—Optimal Capacity Increment as Function of Discount Rate

For given values of r and a, optimal plant size decreases as p increases, and the minimum size is obtained for the no-import case. Similarly, optimal plant size increases as k increases.

The behaviour of x^* as the discount rate r varies is shown in Figure 10.3 for several values of kD^a/pD. For the no-import case, it was noted that x^* decreases with increases in r. This is no longer true if $kD^a/pD > 0$. That is, if p is finite, x^* will decrease and then increase as r increases. A partial explanation of this is given by the lower bound $x' = \dfrac{1}{D}\left(\dfrac{rk}{p}\right)^{1/1-a}$ found for x^*. As r becomes large, this bound must eventually cause x^* to become large. If a is close to 1, the response will be more pronounced. A particular value of x^* may correspond to two values of r: r_1 and r_2. In this situation, since $\dfrac{y_1^*}{y_2^*} = \dfrac{r_1}{r_2}$, the optimal policy is distinguished by the corresponding values of y^*, the duration of the temporary import phase.

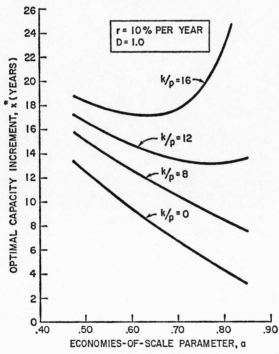

Figure 10.4.—Optimal Capacity Increment as Function of Economies-of-Scale Parameter

Response of x^* to changes in the economies-of-scale parameter a is more difficult to characterize since the term kD^a/pD changes as a varies. The influence of a on this term is eliminated for $D = 1$; for this case Figure 10.4 relates x^* and a for several values of k/p. The ratio $\dfrac{rk}{p}$ is critical in determining the response of x^* to a. If $\dfrac{rk}{p} > 1$, the lower bound $\dfrac{1}{D}\left(\dfrac{rk}{p}\right)^{1/1-a}$ indicates that x^* becomes large as a approaches 1. For this case, x^* will decrease and then increase as a increases. This counter-example rules out the plausible supposition that more pronounced economies-of-scale should always lead to larger plant sizes. In the limiting case $a = 1$, plant investment costs are linear (no economies-of-scale) and it will be optimal to construct capacity (continuously) only if $\dfrac{rk}{p} \leqslant 1$. For $\dfrac{rk}{p} \leqslant 1$, this suggests that as a increases, x^* decreases monotonically to zero in a manner similar to that of the no-import case.

APPENDIX A

A REGENERATION POINT THEOREM

In this appendix we will show that an optimal solution to the plant size model with time-phased imports has the property that $y^* \leqslant x^*$, provided that some plant size is admissible as defined by (10.1). This is known as the *regeneration point property* since between any two points in time at which plant capacity is constructed, there is a point at which demand equals the capacity installed, or *point of regeneration*. It will also be shown that the number of decision variables may be reduced by a preliminary optimization step which defines y for each admissible x. The proofs will be given for the general case of non-stationary rates of demand growth $D(t) \geqslant 0$.

In the non-stationary demand growth rate case, z_i will denote the size of the ith plant constructed. The admissibility criterion (10.1) becomes

$$f(z_i) \leqslant \frac{p}{r} z_i$$

Looking forward from a point of regeneration, we define y_i as the time elapsed before the ith plant is constructed. Let $\Pi = ((z_1,y_1),(z_2,y_2), \ldots)$ denote a policy for constructing plants over an infinite horizon. We designate the total discounted costs of following policy Π from time t as $C(\Pi,t)$. Assuming that $D(t)$ is integrable, the number of years of demand growth x_1 that plant size z_1 will supply is defined by

$$z_1 = \int_0^{x_1} D(t)dt$$

With this notation, we now prove the following result.

Regeneration point theorem[1,2]

Assume that a regeneration point occurs at time $t = 0$, and that $f(\cdot)$ is such that some values of zi are admissible. In an optimal policy Π^* with optimal decisions designated (z_i^*, y_i^*), the following properties hold:

(i) $y_1^* \leqslant x_1^*$

(ii) $\displaystyle\int_0^{y_1^*} D(t)dt = \frac{rf(z_1^*)}{p}$

Proof:

(i) Suppose that $y_1^* \geqslant x_1^*$. Restricting our analysis to policies Π with $y_1 \geqslant x_1$, we may write

$$C(\Pi, 0) = \begin{bmatrix} \text{discounted cost of importing} \\ \text{to satisfy demand until first} \\ \text{plant is constructed} \end{bmatrix} + \begin{bmatrix} \text{discounted} \\ \text{construction cost of} \\ \text{first plant} \end{bmatrix}$$

$$+ \begin{bmatrix} \text{discounted cost of supplying the constant level of demand} \\ \text{outstanding after construction of first plant during the} \\ \text{period between construction of first and second plants} \end{bmatrix}$$

$$+ \begin{bmatrix} \text{discounted cost of supplying demand growth between} \\ \text{construction of first and second plants} \end{bmatrix}$$

$$+ \begin{bmatrix} \text{discounted construction} \\ \text{cost of second plant} \end{bmatrix} + \begin{bmatrix} \text{discounted costs after} \\ \text{construction of second} \\ \text{plant} \end{bmatrix}$$

---

[1] Property (i) is noted in Hadley and Whitin (1963), p. 43, for a similar stationary problem in inventory theory in which average annual cost is minimized. The author is indebted to T. N. Srinivasan for pointing out that an earlier proof of property (ii) developed for the case $f(z) = k(z)^a$ was valid for more general investment cost functions.

[2] The reader may find it interesting to note the similarity in results and differences in assumptions between this theorem and the regeneration point theorem in chapter 11 below.

or,

$$C(\Pi, 0) = \int_0^{y_1}\left[\int_t^{y_1}pe^{-rs}ds\right]D(t)dt + e^{-ry_1}f(z_1)$$

$$+ \int_{y_1}^{y_2}p\left[\int_0^{y_1}D(s)ds - z_1\right]e^{-rt}dt + \int_{y_1}^{y_2}\left[\int_t^{y_2}pe^{-rs}ds\right]D(t)dt$$

$$+ e^{-ry_2}f(z_2) + e^{-ry_2}C(\Pi, y_2)$$

We have $y_1 \leqslant y_2$ by definition, and since the case $y_1 \geqslant x_1$ is being considered, the level of demand outstanding after construction of the first plant is non-negative. Holding y_2, z_1, and z_2 constant and differentiating partially with respect to y_1, we have

$$\frac{\partial C(\Pi, 0)}{\partial y_1} = \int_0^{y_1}pD(t)e^{-ry_1}dt - re^{-ry_1}f(z_1)$$

$$+ \int_{y_1}^{y_2}pD(y_1)e^{-rt}dt - pe^{-ry_1}\left[\int_0^{y_1}D(s)ds - z_1\right]$$

$$- \int_{y_1}^{y_2}pD(y_1)e^{-rs}ds$$

$$= e^{-ry_1}[pz_1 - rf(z_1)]$$

Since z_1 is an admissible plant size, $\dfrac{\partial C(\Pi, 0)}{\partial y_1} \geqslant 0$. By decreasing y_1 in the

direction of x_1, we do not increase $C(\Pi, 0)$. Hence $y_1^* = x_1^*$ is optimal, and among all policies Π, $y_1^* \leqslant x_1^*$ will be optimal.

(ii) From (i), we now may restrict our analysis to policies Π with $y_1 \leqslant x_1$, and we have

$$C(\Pi, 0) = \int_0^{y_1}\left[\int_t^{y_1}pe^{-rs}ds\right]D(t)dt + e^{-ry_1}f(z_1) + e^{-rx_1}C(\Pi, x_1)$$

Differentiating partially with respect to y_1, we obtain

$$\frac{\partial C(\Pi, 0)}{\partial y_1} = e^{-ry_1}\left[p\int_0^{y_1}D(t)dt - rf(z_1)\right]$$

Since $D(t)$ is non-negative, $\dfrac{\partial C(\Pi, 0)}{\partial y_1}$ is non-decreasing in y_1 and the unconstrained minimum is at

$$\int_0^{y_1(z_1)} D(t)dt = \frac{rf(z_1)}{p} \qquad \ldots \ldots \quad (10.1 \text{ A})$$

For any admissible z_1,

$$z_1 = \int_0^{x_1} D(t)dt \geqslant \frac{rf(z_1)}{p} = \int_0^{y_1(z_1)} D(t)dt$$

and $D(t) \geqslant 0$ requires that $y_1(z_1) \leqslant x_1$. Therefore (10.1 A) will hold for all admissible z_1 and in particular the optimal z_1^*, which completes the proof.

Corollary

For any $j \geqslant 2$, $y_{j-1}^* \leqslant \sum_{i=1}^{j-1} x_i^* \leqslant y_j^*$

Proof:

The corollary states that a point of regeneration at $\sum_{i=1}^{j-1} x_i^*$ occurs between each adjoining pair of plant construction decisions. The proof is obvious by reapplying the regeneration point theorem from each successive point of regeneration and noting that it is never optimal to build a plant when excess capacity exists.

Remark 1

By defining $D(t) = 0$ for all $t > T$, we see that the above results hold for a problem with finite horizon T.

Remark 2

Additional meaning is given to expression (10.1 A) if we rewrite it as

$$\left(\frac{p}{r}\right) \int_0^{y_1(z_1)} D(t)dt = f(z_1)$$

Since $\frac{p}{r}$ is the discounted cost for perpetually importing one demand unit, the increment of demand up to $y_1(z_1)$ is the 'breakeven' level of operation for a plant of size z_1.

In the stationary case with $D(t) = D$ for all t, all plant sizes z_1 are the same, and from each point of regeneration the temporary import phase has the same duration. We may write $z = xD$ and (10.1 A) becomes

$$D \int_0^{y(x)} dt = \frac{rf(xD)}{p}$$

Integrating and dividing by D, we have

$$y(x) = \frac{rf(xD)}{pD}$$

as the expression defining the optimal y for any admissible x.

APPENDIX B

COMPUTATION OF OPTIMAL CAPACITIES

Tables 10.1a–10.1e give the results of numerical computation of optimal solutions to the plant size model with time-phased imports for the case with $f(xD) = k(xD)^a$. With the exception of cases where optimal capacities were too large to be of interest, solutions are provided for all combinations of the following parameter values: $a = 0\cdot50$, $0\cdot60$, $0\cdot65$, $0\cdot70$, $0\cdot80$; $r = 0\cdot05$, $0\cdot10$, $0\cdot15$, $0\cdot20$; and $k/p = 0$, 1, 2, 4, 8, 12, 16, 20. Optimal capacity increments were computed by using a variant of the method of Fibonacci search[1] to evaluate directly the minimum of expression (10.5). An alternative approach to computing x^* would be use of interval bisection on (10.11), but the Fibonacci search approach was quite efficient since preparing Tables 10.1a–10.1e required a total computational time of slightly more than one-half minute on the Stanford University IBM 7090 computer. For each set of parameters, the optimal capacity increment x^*, the corresponding optimal duration of the temporary import phase y^*, and the optimal discounted cost value $C(x^*, y^*)/k$ are given for the normalized demand value $D = 1$. The last two columns in each table indicate the sensitivity of the cost level to non-optimal choices of x; these values give the percentage increase in costs for capacity increments of $x^*/2$ and $2x^*$ with y adjusted optimally with respect to the value of x used.

An example will illustrate use of the tables. Suppose that we want to compute the optimal plant size for Indian aluminium plants. According to chapter 3 above, demand is growing at the constant rate of 30 thousand tons per year. Investment costs for an aluminium plant are Rs. $14\cdot4$ $(xD)^{0\cdot77} \times 10^6$ for a plant of size (xD) thousand tons, including allowance for future replacement costs. Aluminium may be imported at a cost of Rs. 2,350 per ton at official exchange rates, and operating expenditures for domestic production will be Rs. 1,720 per ton. It is desired to apply a shadow premium for foreign exchange of 50% above official exchange rates, and there is a 40% import component in the plant investment cost.

---

[1] This method is described in Wilde (1964); also in Bellman and Dreyfus (1962).

TABLE 10.1a

Optimal capacity solutions with time-phased imports
(Economies-of-scale parameter a = 0·50)

Discount rate (r)	Penalty factor (k/p)	Optimal capacity increment (x*)	Optimal temporary import phase (y*)	Minimum discounted costs (C(x*,y*)/k)	Percent increase in costs for capacity increment of	
					(x*/2)	(2x*)
0·05	0·00	25·13	0·00	7·008	8·4	10·1
	1·00	25·33	0·25	6·964	8·5	10·0
	2·00	25·54	0·51	6·920	8·5	10·0
	4·00	25·95	1·02	6·834	8·5	9·9
	8·00	26·86	2·07	6·662	8·4	9·8
	12·00	27·77	3·16	6·494	8·5	9·7
	16·00	28·72	4·29	6·329	8·4	9·5
	20·00	29·70	5·45	6·167	8·4	9·3
0·10	0·00	12·56	0·00	4·955	8·4	10·1
	1·00	12·85	0·36	4·868	8·5	10·0
	2·00	13·17	0·73	4·782	8·4	9·9
	4·00	13·80	1·49	4·612	8·5	9·7
	8·00	15·17	3·12	4·287	8·5	9·2
	12·00	16·69	4·90	3·979	8·4	8·6
	16·00	18·37	6·86	3·690	8·3	7·9
	20·00	20·23	9·00	3·418	8·2	7·2
0·15	0·00	8·38	0·00	4·046	8·4	10·1
	1·00	8·75	0·44	3·916	8·4	9·9
	2·00	9·13	0·91	3·788	8·5	9·7
	4·00	9·96	1·89	3·543	8·5	9·3
	8·00	11·87	4·13	3·088	8·4	8·1
	12·00	14·16	6·77	2·684	8·1	6·7
	16·00	16·90	9·87	2·330	7·7	5·2
	20·00	20·17	13·47	2·026	7·0	3·6
0·20	0·00	6·28	0·00	3·504	8·4	10·1
	1·00	6·71	0·52	3·331	8·5	9·8
	2·00	7·18	1·07	3·165	8·5	9·5
	4·00	8·21	2·29	2·850	8·4	8·7
	8·00	10·77	5·25	2·298	8·1	6·6
	12·00	14·14	9·03	1·850	7·3	4·2
	16·00	18·51	13·77	1·500	6·0	2·1
	20·00	24·03	19·61	1·235	4·9	0·8

TABLE 10.1b

Optimal capacity solutions with time-phased imports
(Economies-of-scale parameter a = 0·60)

Discount rate (r)	Penalty factor (k/p)	Optimal capacity increment (x*)	Optimal temporary import phase (y*)	Minimum discounted costs (C(x*, y*)/k)	Percent increase in cost for capacity increment (x*/2)	(2x*)
0·05	0·00	18·95	0·00	9·541	7·1	9·2
	1·00	19·22	0·29	9·472	7·0	9·2
	2·00	19·45	0·59	9·402	7·1	9·2
	4·00	20·00	1·21	9·264	7·1	9·1
	8·00	21·12	2·49	8·988	7·1	9·0
	12·00	22·31	3·87	8·715	7·1	8·8
	16·00	23·60	5·33	8·445	7·1	8·7
	20·00	24·96	6·89	8·178	7·1	8·4
0·10	0·00	9·47	0·00	6·295	7·1	9·2
	1·00	9·81	0·39	6·174	7·1	9·1
	2·00	10·17	0·80	6·053	7·1	9·1
	4·00	10·93	1·68	5·815	7·1	8·9
	8·00	12·68	3·67	5·347	7·1	8·4
	12·00	14·77	6·04	4·894	7·1	7·7
	16·00	17·28	8·84	4·462	7·0	6·8
	20·00	20·29	12·17	4·053	6·9	5·7
0·15	0·00	6·32	0·00	4·936	7·1	9·2
	1·00	6·72	0·47	4·768	7·1	9·1
	2·00	7·17	0·98	4·603	7·1	8·9
	4·00	8·16	2·11	4·278	7·1	8·5
	8·00	10·69	4·97	3·656	7·1	7·2
	12·00	14·18	8·84	3·088	6·8	5·4
	16·00	18·99	14·04	2·590	6·1	3·2
	20·00	25·54	20·96	2·174	5·0	1·4
0·20	0·00	4·74	0·00	4·153	7·1	9·2
	1·00	5·20	0·54	3·943	7·1	9·0
	2·00	5·73	1·14	3·737	7·1	8·7
	4·00	6·99	2·57	3·335	7·1	8·0
	8·00	10·61	6·60	2·602	6·8	5·4
	12·00	16·45	12·88	1·999	5·6	2·2
	16·00	25·57	22·38	1·554	3·9	0·4
	20·00	38·96	36·01	1·250	1·8	0·0

TABLE 10.1c

Optimal capacity solutions with time-phased imports
(Economies-of-scale parameter $a = 0.65$)

Discount rate (r)	Penalty factor (k/p)	Optimal capacity increment (x^*)	Optimal temporary import phase (y^*)	Minimum discounted costs $(C(x^*, y^*)/k)$	Percent increase in costs for capacity increment of $(x^*/2)$	$(2x^*)$
0·05	0·00	16·15	0·00	11·010	6·3	8·5
	1·00	16·40	0·31	10·926	6·3	8·5
	2·00	16·71	0·62	10·842	6·3	8·5
	4·00	17·28	1·27	10·674	6·3	8·4
	8·00	18·50	2·67	10·337	6·4	8·3
	12·00	19·86	4·19	10·000	6·4	8·2
	16·00	21·35	5·85	9·664	6·4	8·0
	20·00	22·98	7·67	9·328	6·4	7·8
0·10	0·00	8·07	0·00	7·016	6·3	8·5
	1·00	8·43	0·40	6·880	6·3	8·5
	2·00	8·80	0·82	6·743	6·3	8·4
	4·00	9·62	1·74	6·470	6·4	8·2
	8·00	11·57	3·93	5·924	6·4	7·8
	12·00	14·05	6·69	5·384	6·4	7·0
	16·00	17·23	10·18	4·859	6·3	6·0
	20·00	21·33	14·62	4·357	6·1	4·6
0·15	0·00	5·38	0·00	5·391	6·3	8·5
	1·00	5·80	0·47	5·209	6·3	8·4
	2·00	6·26	0·99	5·028	6·3	8·3
	4·00	7·33	2·19	4·665	6·4	7·9
	8·00	10·28	5·46	3·950	6·4	6·6
	12·00	14·80	10·38	3·278	6·0	4·4
	16·00	21·79	17·79	2·687	5·0	1·9
	20·00	32·40	28·77	2·210	3·7	0·5
0·20	0·00	4·04	0·00	4·471	6·3	8·5
	1·00	4·51	0·53	4·249	6·3	8·4
	2·00	5·05	1·15	4·027	6·4	8·1
	4·00	6·43	2·68	3·585	6·4	7·4
	8·00	10·89	7·55	2·746	6·0	4·5
	12·00	19·33	16·45	2·049	4·5	1·2
	16·00	34·49	31·96	1·561	2·1	0·1
	20·00	59·15	56·73	1·250	0·4	0·0

TABLE 10.1d

Optimal capacity solutions with time-phased imports
(Economies-of-scale parameter a = 0·70)

Discount rate (r)	Penalty factor (k/p)	Optimal capacity increment (x^*)	Optimal temporary import phase (y^*)	Minimum discounted costs ($C(x^*, y^*)/k$)	Percent increase in co for capacity increment	
					($x^*/2$)	($2x^*$)
0·05	0·00	13·51	0·00	12·598	5·5	7·7
	1·00	13·79	0·31	12·500	5·5	7·6
	2·00	14·08	0·64	12·402	5·5	7·6
	4·00	14·69	1·31	12·205	5·5	7·6
	8·00	16·02	2·79	11·806	5·5	7·5
	12·00	17·53	4·46	11·401	5·6	7·4
	16·00	19·24	6·34	10·991	5·6	7·2
	20·00	21·19	8·48	10·576	5·6	7·0
0·10	0·00	6·75	0·00	7·755	5·5	7·7
	1·00	7·11	0·39	7·606	5·5	7·6
	2·00	7·49	0·82	7·457	5·5	7·6
	4·00	8·35	1·77	7·153	5·5	7·4
	8·00	10·51	4·15	6·530	5·6	7·0
	12·00	13·52	7·43	5·893	5·6	6·2
	16·00	17·73	11·97	5·255	5·5	5·0
	20·00	23·73	18·35	4·634	5·1	3·3
0·15	0·00	4·50	0·00	5·839	5·5	7·7
	1·00	4·91	0·46	5·649	5·5	7·6
	2·00	5·38	0·97	5·456	5·5	7·5
	4·00	6·52	2·23	5·061	5·6	7·2
	8·00	9·99	6·01	4·250	5·6	5·8
	12·00	16·22	12·66	3·452	5·1	3·2
	16·00	27·58	24·47	2·751	3·8	0·7
	20·00	47·63	44·83	2·221	1·7	0·0
0·20	0·00	3·38	0·00	4·774	5·5	7·7
	1·00	3·84	0·51	4·547	5·5	7·5
	2·00	4·39	1·13	4·315	5·6	7·4
	4·00	5·89	2·77	3·839	5·6	6·7
	8·00	11·60	8·90	2·881	5·2	3·5
	12·00	25·20	22·97	2·076	3·1	0·3
	16·00	54·58	52·61	1·562	0·4	0·0

TABLE 10.1e

Optimal capacity solutions with time-phased imports
(*Economies-of-scale parameter a* $= 0 \cdot 80$)

scount rate (r)	Penalty factor (k/p)	Optimal capacity increment (x*)	Optimal temporary import phase (y*)	Minimum discounted costs (C(x*, y*)/k)	Percent increase in costs for capacity increment of	
					(x*/2)	(2x*)
0·05	0·00	8·61	0·00	16·002	3·7	5·5
	1·00	8·89	0·29	15·889	3·7	5·5
	2·00	9·17	0·59	15·774	3·7	5·5
	4·00	9·76	1·24	15·540	3·8	5·5
	8·00	11·20	2·76	15·048	3·8	5·4
	12·00	12·98	4·66	14·523	3·8	5·4
	16·00	15·24	7·07	13·961	3·9	5·2
	20·00	18·17	10·17	13·360	3·9	5·0
0·10	0·00	4·31	0·00	9·190	3·7	5·5
	1·00	4·63	0·34	9·040	3·7	5·5
	2·00	4·98	0·72	8·884	3·8	5·5
	4·00	5·84	1·64	8·555	3·8	5·4
	8·00	8·44	4·41	7·816	3·9	5·1
	12·00	13·25	9·48	6·953	3·9	4·2
	16·00	23·02	19·67	5·973	3·6	2·2
	20·00	44·55	41·70	4·981	2·4	0·3
0·15	0·00	2·87	0·00	6·645	3·7	5·5
	1·00	3·23	0·38	6·466	3·8	5·5
	2·00	3·67	0·85	6·276	3·8	5·5
	4·00	4·86	2·13	5·860	3·9	5·3
	8·00	10·05	7·60	4·854	3·9	3·8
	12·00	27·32	25·38	3·683	2·6	0·5
	16·00	86·70	85·24	2·778	0·1	0·0
0·20	0·00	2·15	0·00	5·279	3·7	5·5
	1·00	2·55	0·42	5·075	3·8	5·5
	2·00	3·07	0·98	4·855	3·8	5·4
	4·00	4·78	2·80	4·350	3·9	4·9
	8·00	16·86	15·33	3·085	3·0	0·9
	12·00	85·81	84·54	2·083	0·0	0·0

The discount rate is 10% per year. To compute the optimal plant size, duration of the temporary import phase, and discounted costs using the tables, we proceed as follows:

(1) Compute the adjusted penalty cost p, the difference between import cost adjusted for the foreign exchange premium and domestic operating expenditures.

$$p = (1 \cdot 5)(2{,}350) - (1{,}720) = \text{Rs. } 1{,}805/\text{ton} = \text{Rs. } 1{,}805 \times 10^3/\text{thousand tons}$$

(2) Adjust k, in the investment cost formula $k(xD)^a$, for the foreign exchange premium.

$$k' = [0 \cdot 6 + (0 \cdot 4)(1 \cdot 5)]\, 14 \cdot 4 \times 10^6 = 17 \cdot 3 \times 10^6$$

(3) Compute the penalty factor equivalent to k/p in the case of $D = 1 \cdot 0$.

$$\frac{k'D^a}{pD} = \frac{17 \cdot 3 \times 10^6}{(1{,}805 \times 10^3)\,(30)^{0 \cdot 23}} = 4 \cdot 38$$

(4) From tables 10.1d and 10.1e, compute the normalized optimal plant size by interpolation for $a = 0 \cdot 77$, $r = 0 \cdot 10$, and $k/p = 4 \cdot 38$. Using tabular form for interpolation, we have:

a \ k/p	4	4·38	8
0·70	8·35		10·51
0·77	6·59	6·82	9·06
0·80	5·84		8·44

The optimal cycle time x^* is $6 \cdot 8$ years, and the optimal plant size is $(x^*D) = (6 \cdot 8)(30) = 204$ thousand tons/year.

(5) Find the optimal duration of the temporary import phase y^*, using equation (10.4).

$$y^* = \frac{rk(xD)^a}{pD} = (0 \cdot 10)(4 \cdot 38)(6 \cdot 8)^{0 \cdot 77} = 1 \cdot 92 \text{ years}$$

(6) Compute the optimal discounted cost per ton of demand using (10.6):

$$s(x^*, y^*) = p\left[\frac{1 - e^{-ry*}}{1 - e^{-rx*}}\right] = 1{,}805\left[\frac{1 - e^{-0 \cdot 192}}{1 - e^{-0 \cdot 68}}\right]$$

$$= \text{Rs. } 638/\text{ton}$$

Adding operating costs, total costs per ton of aluminium are Rs. 2,358/ton.

(7) Costs may be separated into components of domestic cost, exchange cost at the official rate, and exchange premium cost as follows:

Source	Domestic cost (Rs./ton)	Foreign exchange cost (official rate) (Rs./ton)
Plant construction*	290	193
Operating costs†	1,664	—
Product imports‡	—	76
Totals	1,954	269

* Total plant construction cost/ton $= \dfrac{r^2}{D} \left[\dfrac{e^{-ry}k(xD)^a}{1 - e^{-rx}} \right]$

(allocated to domestic and imported portions)

† Domestic operating costs $= c - \dfrac{r^2}{D} \left[\dfrac{1}{1 - e^{-rx}} \right] \displaystyle\int_0^y c(tD)e^{-rt}dt$

$= c - c \left[\dfrac{1 - e^{-ry}(1 + ry)}{1 - e^{-rx}} \right]$

where c is the operating cost/ton.

‡ Product import costs $= \dfrac{r^2}{D} \left[\dfrac{1}{1 - e^{-rx}} \right] \displaystyle\int_0^y i(tD)e^{-rt}dt$

$= i \left[\dfrac{1 - e^{-ry}(1 + ry)}{1 - e^{-rx}} \right]$

where i is the import cost/ton at the official exchange rate.

The difference between the total cost obtained in Step 6, Rs. 2,358, and the sum of the domestic cost and official exchange cost, Rs. 2,223, is the 50% exchange premium cost component, Rs. 135.

REFERENCES

Bellman, R. E., and S. E. Dreyfus, *Applied Dynamic Programming*, Princeton University Press, Princeton, N. J., 1962, Chapter IV.

Hadley, G., and T. M. Whitin, *Analysis of Inventory Systems*, Prentice-Hall, Inc., Englewood Cliffs, N. J., 1963.

Manne, A. S., 'Capacity Expansion and Probabilistic Growth', *Econometrica*, October 1961.

Wilde, D. J., *Optimum Seeking Methods*, Prentice-Hall, Inc., Englewood Cliffs, N. J., 1964, Chapter 2.

M

CHAPTER 11

OPTIMAL PLANT SIZE WITH ARBITRARY INCREASING TIME PATHS OF DEMAND

ALAN S. MANNE

and

ARTHUR F. VEINOTT, JR.

This chapter presents a technique for calculating optimal sizes of plant capacity to be added within a single producing area at each of a finite number of points in time. The demands for capacity are assumed to be non-decreasing over time, but are otherwise arbitrary. The analysis of the model is based on certain properties of convex sets and concave functions which are recorded below.

Some properties of convex sets and concave functions

Let V be a subset of n-dimensional Euclidean space. We say that V is *convex* if for each two distinct points v and $\bar{v}$ in V and for all $\alpha, \beta \geqslant 0$, $\alpha + \beta = 1$, the point $V \equiv \alpha v + \beta \bar{v}$ is also in V. A point v in a convex set V is called an *extreme point* of V if there do not exist two distinct points v and $\bar{v}$ in V such that $v = (1/2)v + (1/2)\bar{v}$. For an account of useful properties of convex sets see Hadley (1961, Chapter 6) or Charnes and Cooper (1961, pp. 233–45, 274–82).

A real-valued function $C(\cdot)$ defined on a convex set V is said to be *concave* if for each two distinct points v and $\bar{v}$ in V and for all $\alpha, \beta \geqslant 0$ with $\alpha + \beta = 1$, then

$$C(\alpha v + \beta \bar{v}) \geqslant \alpha C(v) + \beta C(\bar{v}).$$

Some of the properties of concave functions are developed in Hadley (1964, Chapter 3, Sections 10–12).

The following known properties of convex sets and concave functions will be employed in the sequel.

P1: If $C(\cdot)$ is concave on a closed, bounded convex set V having finitely many extreme points, then $C(\cdot)$ achieves its minimum on V at an extreme point of V.[1]

[1] This result may be proved as follows. Let $e_1, \ldots, e_m$ denote the extreme points of V. We suppose the extreme points are labelled so that $C(e_1) = \min_{1 \leqslant i \leqslant m} C(e_i)$.

Remark: In searching for a minimum of $C(\cdot)$ over V, P1 implies that no loss of optimality occurs if we confine our search to the extreme points of V.

P2: Sums of concave functions are concave.[1]

P3: The set of solutions to a finite system of *linear* equalities and inequalities is a convex set and has finitely many extreme points.[2]

P4: A concave function of a linear function is concave.[3]

Model formulation

Time is idealized as though it consists of discrete periods numbered $1, 2, \ldots, T$. The demand increment that takes place in period t, i.e. the difference between the demands in periods t and $t-1$, is a known constant, D_t. It is assumed that $D_t \geqslant 0$, $t = 1, \ldots, T$. Also $\sum_{t=1}^{T} D_t > 0$.

The decision variable v_t denotes the size of plant capacity built in period t. The vector v is the sequence of T unknowns $(v_1, v_2, \ldots, v_T)$, and is called a *capacity schedule*. The variables z_t denote the end-of-period excess capacities (which may be positive, zero, or negative), and are defined in terms of the v_t and D_t as follows:

$$z_0 = 0$$

$$z_t = \sum_{j=1}^{t} (v_j - D_j) \, (t = 1, \ldots, T) \quad \ldots \quad (11.1)$$

We say that the capacity schedule v is *feasible* if:

$$v \geqslant 0 \quad \ldots \quad \ldots \quad (11.2)$$

and

$$z_T = 0 \quad \ldots \quad \ldots \quad (11.3)$$

It is known (see for example, Hadley (1961, p.217) or Charnes and Cooper (1961, pp. 280–81)) that each v in V can be expressed in the form

$$v = \sum_{i=1}^{m} \alpha_i e_i \text{ where } \alpha_i \geqslant 0, i = 1, 2, \ldots, m \text{ and } \sum_{i=1}^{m} \alpha_i = 1.$$

Then from the definition of a concave function it follows easily that

$$C(v) \geqslant \sum_{i=1}^{m} \alpha_i C(e_i) \geqslant C(e_1).$$

Thus e_1 minimizes $C(\cdot)$ over V, which completes the proof.

[1] See Hadley (1964, p. 85) for a proof.

[2] See Hadley (1961, pp. 204–5) for a proof of the first assertion. The second assertion is proved in Charnes and Cooper (1961, p. 245).

[3] The proof is a simple consequence of the definition of a concave function.

Let V denote the set of feasible capacity schedules. From (11.1)–(11.3) and P3, we conclude that V forms a closed, bounded convex set.

Let $C(v)$ represent the cost associated with the capacity schedule v. The function $C(v)$ is expressed in terms of the present value of costs as of time 1. For each period t, we shall assume that there are two cost elements: the construction costs and the temporary import penalty costs. These elements may be zero or positive in value. The plant construction costs depend upon v_t, the size of unit built during period t. The construction costs in period t are expressed as a function $C_t(v_t)$. The temporary import penalty costs are proportional to the negative excess capacity—if any. Letting p_t denote the constant of proportionality for period t, these penalty costs are: $p_t \max(0, -z_t)$, with $p_t > 0$. The total costs may then be expressed as the following sum:

$$C(v) = \sum_{t=1}^{T} C_t(v_t) + \sum_{t=1}^{T} p_t \max(0, -z_t) \quad . \quad . \quad . \quad (11.4)$$

It is assumed that each individual construction cost function $C_t(\cdot)$ is concave. Examples of such concave functions are provided in Figures (11.1) and (11.2)—respectively a power function and a power function pieced together with a linear segment. These two would provide acceptable idealizations of investment costs within

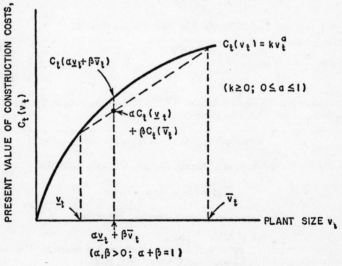

Figure 11.1.—A Concave Function

any of the four Indian industries described in this volume. Figure (11.3) illustrates one type of cost function which is eliminated by the assumption of concavity. This staircase structure would be of

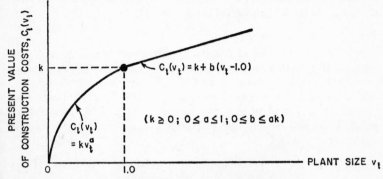

Figure 11.2.—A Concave Function

practical interest if a plant's capacity could only be expanded through integral multiples of one standard-sized unit.

A feasible capacity schedule will be called *optimal* if it minimizes $C(\cdot)$ over V. In the next section we shall characterize the structure

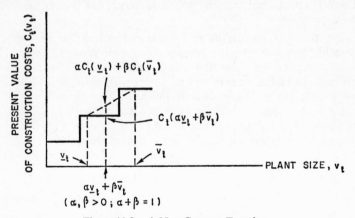

Figure 11.3.—A Non-Concave Function

of an optimal schedule under the assumption that $C(\cdot)$ takes the form (11.4) where each function $C_t(\cdot)$ is concave and $p_t \geqslant 0$, $t = 1$, ..., T. The proof is carried out in such a way as to cover also the more general cost function:

$$C(v) = P(v) + \sum_{t=1}^{T} p_t(z_t) \qquad \ldots \quad (11.5)$$

where $P(\cdot)$ is concave on V, and where the functions $p_t(\cdot)$ are concave on the interval $(-\infty, 0]$ and on the interval $[0, +\infty)$, but not necessarily on the interval $(-\infty, +\infty)$.

The regeneration point theorem

A *point of regeneration* of a capacity schedule v is said to occur in period t if $z_t = 0$. For a feasible capacity schedule v, such a point necessarily occurs in period 0 and T. A feasible capacity schedule v is said to have the *regeneration point property* if between any two periods in which plant capacity is added, there is a regeneration point. Formally, we say that a feasible v has the above property if whenever $i < k$ and

$$v_i > 0; v_{i+1} = v_{i+2} = \ldots = v_{k-1} = 0; \text{ and } v_k > 0, \quad . \quad (11.6)$$

there exists a period t, $i \leqslant t \leqslant k - 1$, in which there occurs a regeneration point.

The importance of the regeneration point property lies in the following result.

Regeneration point theorem

There is an optimal capacity schedule which has the regeneration point property.

The theorem permits us to confine our search for an optimal schedule to those with the regeneration point property. In a subsequent section we show how the schedules with the regeneration point property can be searched efficiently with a dynamic programming recursion to find one that is optimal.

Before proving the theorem we need some preliminary definitions and lemmas. Although $C(\cdot)$ need not be concave on V, as we shall see, $C(\cdot)$ is concave on the following convex subset of V, called a *basic set*,

$$V_{i_1 \ldots i_{T-1}} = \{v | v \epsilon V \text{ and } (-1)^{i_t}(z_t) \geqslant 0 \text{ for } t = 1, \ldots, T-1\}$$

where each subscript i_t is 0 or $+1$. The 2^{T-1} such sets are identified by the $T - 1$ subscripts i_t. Also z_t is non-negative or non-positive according as i_t is 0 or $+1$. As a specific illustration, suppose $T = 3$. Then the four basic sets are:

$$V_{00} = \{v | v \epsilon V, z_1 \geqslant 0, z_2 \geqslant 0\}, \quad V_{01} = \{v | v \epsilon V, z_1 \geqslant 0, z_2 \leqslant 0\},$$
$$V_{10} = \{v | v \epsilon V, z_1 \leqslant 0, z_2 \geqslant 0\}, \quad V_{11} = \{v | v \epsilon V, z_1 \leqslant 0, z_2 \leqslant 0\}.$$

The basic set $V_{00\ldots 0}$ is of special interest because it consists of precisely those feasible schedules in which no temporary imports are required.

Lemma 1

There is an optimal capacity schedule which is an extreme point of some basic set.

Proof:

Clearly V is the union of the 2^{T-1} basic sets. These sets are closed, bounded convex sets having finitely many extreme points by P3. Moreover, by P2, P4, and (11.4) or (11.5), it is clear that $C(\cdot)$ is concave on each basic set (although not necessarily on V). By P1, $C(\cdot)$ achieves its minimum on each basic set at an extreme point of that set. Consequently, $C(\cdot)$ achieves its minimum on V at an extreme point of some basic set, which completes the proof.

Lemma 2

Each extreme point of each basic set has the regeneration point property.

Proof:

The proof is by contraposition. Suppose there is a feasible v that does not have the regeneration point property. Then there are time periods i and k such that (11.6) holds and $z_t \neq 0$ for all periods t, with $i \leqslant t \leqslant k-1$. We now show that v cannot be an extreme point of any basic set. This is done by generating two distinct alternative vectors $\bar{v}$ and $\underline{v}$ within the same basic set as v, and showing that v may be formed by taking one-half the sum of these two. Hence v cannot be an extreme point.

Let
$$\epsilon = \min \left[v_i, v_k, \min_{i \leqslant t \leqslant k-1} |z_t| \right].$$

By (11.6) and the assumption that $z_t \neq 0$ for all t over the interval $i \leqslant t \leqslant k-1$, it follows that $\epsilon > 0$. Let u_t be a T-component vector having the element $+1$ in the tth position and zeros elsewhere. Define two distinct alternative schedules to v, denoted $\bar{v}$ and $\underline{v}$, by

$$\bar{v} = v + \epsilon (u_i - u_k)$$

and

$$\underline{v} = v - \epsilon (u_i - u_k).$$

Let the vectors $(\bar{z}_t)$ and $(\underline{z}_t)$ denote the excess capacities associated with the alternative schedules $\bar{v}$ and $\underline{v}$ respectively. From the definition of ϵ, it follows that $\bar{v}$ and $\underline{v}$ are feasible. Moreover, for $t < i$ and for $t \geqslant k, z_t = \underline{z}_t = \bar{z}_t$.

For $i \leqslant t \leqslant k - 1$, $\bar{z}_t = z_t + \epsilon$ and $\underline{z}_t = z_t - \epsilon$. (See Figure 11.4.) Consequently, if z_t is non-positive (non-negative), then both $\bar{z}_t$ and $\underline{z}_t$ are also non-positive (non-negative). Therefore, if v lies in a specified basic set, then so do $\underline{v}$ and $\bar{v}$. But $\underline{v} \neq \bar{v}$ and $v = (1/2)\underline{v} + (1/2)\bar{v}$. Hence v cannot be an extreme point of the specified basic set. This completes the proof.

Remark: The converse of Lemma 2 is also true, i.e. any feasible schedule having the regeneration point property must also be an extreme point of some basic set.

The Regeneration Point Theorem now follows immediately from Lemmas 1 and 2.

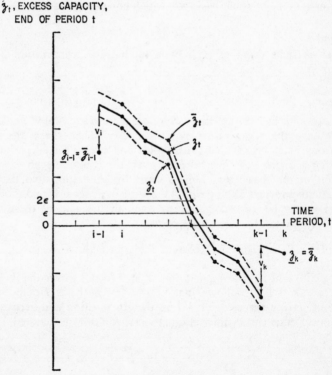

Figure 11.4.—An Excess Capacity Schedule That Does Not Have The Regeneration Point Property

The case of no temporary imports—numerical computations

Up to this point we have assumed that temporary imports are permitted. If we do not allow temporary imports, then the set of admissible schedules will simply be the basic set $V_{00\ldots0}$. It is easy to check that the statements and proofs of Lemmas 1 and 2, and of the Regeneration Point Theorem also hold for this case.[1]

We begin the description of numerical computations by showing how to search the schedules with the regeneration point property to find one that is optimal in the case of no temporary imports. (The other case will be covered in the next section.) Suppose we have a feasible capacity schedule v with the regeneration point property. Let one regeneration point (zero excess capacity) occur at period i and the *next* one at period k (with $i < k$). Then necessarily there is an integer j, $i + 1 \leqslant j \leqslant k$, such that:

$$v_j = \sum_{t=i+1}^{k} D_t \qquad \ldots \ldots \ldots \quad (11.7)$$

$$v_t = 0 \ (t \neq j \text{ and } i + 1 \leqslant t \leqslant k)$$

Moreover, for the case of no temporary imports we must have $j = i + 1$. To see this, suppose $j > i + 1$, so that $k > i + 1$ and also $z_{i+1} = -D_{i+1}$. If $D_{i+1} > 0$, then $z_{i+1} < 0$ and v lies outside the basic set $V_{00\ldots0}$. On the other hand, if $D_{i+1} = 0$, then period $i + 1$ (distinct from period k) is the next regeneration point after period i. Thus in either case we have a contradiction. This proves the following lemma:

Lemma 3

If no temporary imports are permitted, if the feasible capacity schedule v has the regeneration point property, and if two successive regeneration points occur at periods i and k (with $i < k$), then:

$$v_{i+1} = \sum_{t=i+1}^{k} D_t \qquad \ldots \ldots \ldots \quad (11.8)$$

and $\qquad v_t = 0 \ (t = i + 2, \ldots, k).$

---

[1] A form of the Regeneration Point Theorem was first stated independently for the case of no temporary imports by Wagner and Whitin (1958) and Manne (1958). Proofs of a form of the Theorem for this case and special assumptions about $C(\cdot)$ were first given by Wagner and Whitin (1958) and Wagner (1960). A proof for a general concave cost function along the lines given here, i.e. by showing that the extreme points of $V_0 \ldots_0$ have the regeneration point property, was given by Veinott (1963). Forms of Lemmas 1 and 2, the converse of Lemma 2, and the Regeneration Point Theorem were first established for the case where temporary imports are permitted by Zangwill (1965). Our formulation and proofs are based on his work, but seem to be simpler.

From Lemma 3, it follows that if temporary imports are to be zero and if a feasible capacity v has the regeneration point property, then v is uniquely determined by its regeneration points. In view of (11.4), the present value c_{ik} of all costs incurred during periods $i + 1, \ldots, k$ may be computed from:

$$c_{ik} = \sum_{t=i+1}^{k} C_t(v_t) \qquad \cdots \cdots \qquad (11.9)$$

where the v_t are determined by (11.8). Conditions (11.1) and (11.3) guarantee, respectively, that the first regeneration point occurs at period 0 and the last at period T. Hence, in order to calculate the total cost of a feasible capacity schedule with the regeneration point property, we add together the costs c_{ik} associated with each of its successive pairs of regeneration points.

If we identify the regeneration points as nodes and identify the pairs of successive regeneration points as arcs of a network, it follows that our capacity scheduling problem is equivalent to that of finding a minimal cost path (or shortest route) through an acyclic network. Thus an optimal schedule may be found through a special-purpose dynamic programming recursion. (See Wagner and Whitin (1958) and Bellman and Dreyfus (1962, p. 229).) Here we illustrate one form of this recursive optimization procedure—moving backward[1] in time from the horizon date T.

Let f_i be the minimum discounted cost of satisfying the demand increments $D_{i+1}, \ldots, D_T$, given that a regeneration point occurs at period i and that an optimal schedule is followed in periods $i + 1, \ldots, T$. In view of the regeneration point theorem, the f_i may be computed from:

$$f_T = 0$$
$$f_i = \min_{i < k \leqslant T} (c_{ik} + f_k) \qquad \cdots \cdots \qquad (11.10)$$

$$(i = 0, 1, \ldots, T-1).$$

An example:

An illustrative set of numerical computations will not be presented for the zero import case. The input data needed for numerical computations are: the time horizon T, the single period demand in-

---

[1] Alternatively, one might apply a 'forward algorithm'—moving forward in time from the initial date 0.

crements D_t, and the single period construction cost functions $C_t(v_t)$. These parameters and functions[1] are taken to be as follows:

$$T = 6$$

$$D_1 = 0 \cdot 5 \qquad D_4 = 1 \cdot 5$$
$$D_2 = 1 \cdot 0 \qquad D_5 = 1 \cdot 0$$
$$D_3 = 1 \cdot 5 \qquad D_6 = 0 \cdot 5$$

$$\text{For } t = 1, 2, \ldots 6, \ C_t(v_t) = \begin{cases} 0 & \text{if } v_t = 0 \\ 0 \cdot 8^{t-1}(5 + 10v_t) & \text{if } v_t > 0 \end{cases}$$

The resulting cost coefficients c_{ik} are listed in Table 11.1.

The entry c_{06} refers to a capacity schedule in which one regeneration point occurs at time 0, and the next one at time 6. Enough capacity must be built in period 1 to cover the demand increments through period 6. Hence $v_1 = 6 \cdot 0$, and $c_{06} = C_1(v_1) = 65 \cdot 0$.

The entry c_{25} refers to a capacity schedule in which one regeneration point occurs at time 2, and the next one at time 5. Enough capacity must be built in period 3 to cover the demand increments through period 5. Hence $v_3 = 4 \cdot 0$, and $c_{25} = C_3(v_3) = 0 \cdot 8^2(45 \cdot 0) = 28 \cdot 8$.

TABLE 11.1

Matrix of cost coefficients, c_{ik}

regeneration point at i \ Next regeneration point at k	1	2	3	4	5	6
0	10·0	20·0	35·0	50·0	60·0	65·0
1	×	12·0	24·0	36·0	44·0	48·0
2	×	×	12·8	22·4	28·8	32·0
3	×	×	×	10·2	15·4	17·9
4	×	×	×	×	6·2	8·2
5	×	×	×	×	×	3·3

For the numerical example summarized in Table 11.1, the recursion (11.10) would work as follows:[2]

[1] These construction cost functions $C_t(v_t)$ are of the 'fixed charge' type, hence are concave. In the computations that follow, nothing essential depends upon the fact that the undiscounted functions $(5 + 10v_t)$ remain stationary over time.

[2] With T time periods, the total number of numerical calculations for this recursion would be $(T/2)\ (T + 1)$ additions. With electronic equipment, such computations would be quite feasible even if T were of the order of several thousands.

$$f_6 = 0$$

$$f_5 = \min_{5 < k \leqslant 6} (c_{5k} + f_k) = c_{56} + f_6 = 3 \cdot 3$$

$$f_4 = \min_{4 < k \leqslant 6} (c_{4k} + f_k) = c_{46} + f_6 = 8 \cdot 2$$

$$f_3 = \min_{3 < k \leqslant 6} (c_{3k} + f_k) = c_{36} + f_6 = 17 \cdot 9$$

$$f_2 = \min_{2 < k \leqslant 6} (c_{2k} + f_k) = c_{24} + f_4 = 30 \cdot 6$$

$$f_1 = \min_{1 < k \leqslant 6} (c_{1k} + f_k) = c_{13} + f_3 = 41 \cdot 9$$

$$f_0 = \min_{0 < k \leqslant 6} (c_{0k} + f_k) = c_{02} + f_2 = 50 \cdot 6.$$

Since f_0 is computed so as to minimize costs for satisfying the demand increments for periods 1–6, we now know that an optimal schedule will cost $50 \cdot 6$ units over this entire time horizon. Moreover, since

$$
\begin{aligned}
f_0 &= c_{02} + f_2 \\
&= c_{02} + c_{24} + f_4 \\
&= c_{02} + c_{24} + c_{46} + f_6 \\
&= 20 \cdot 0 + 22 \cdot 4 + 8 \cdot 2 + 0 \\
&= 50 \cdot 6,
\end{aligned}
$$

this tells us that the regeneration points in an optimal schedule would occur successively at periods 0, 2, 4 and 6. The optimal capacity schedule v is:

$$
\begin{array}{ll}
v_1 = 1 \cdot 5 & \qquad v_4 = 0 \\
v_2 = 0 & \qquad v_5 = 1 \cdot 5 \\
v_3 = 3 \cdot 0 & \qquad v_6 = 0.
\end{array}
$$

NOTE: For the class of models considered within this chapter, it is purely coincidental that the optimal solution entails a constant cycle time between successive plant installations.

The case of temporary imports—numerical computations

If temporary imports are permitted, the numerical computations become only slightly more laborious. The 'shortest route' dynamic programming recursion is still applicable. Again this algorithm is based upon certain coefficients c_{ik} which represent the costs incurred during the interval between two successive points of regeneration at i and at k. The only difference is that we must now produce the c_{ik} coefficients through a preliminary optimization step in which we minimize the sum of construction and penalty costs over the interval from i to k.

Where temporary imports are permitted, it is not possible to assert (as does Lemma 3) that the index j in (11.7) equals $i + 1$. Instead j may take on any integer value $i + 1, i + 2, \ldots, k$. The construction and penalty costs during the interval from i to k for fixed j are given by:

$$c_{ik}^j = C_j\left(\sum_{t=i+1}^{k} D_t\right) + \sum_{\substack{t=i+1 \\ t \neq j}}^{k} C_t(0) + \sum_{t=i+1}^{j-1} p_t\left(\sum_{\tau=i+1}^{t} D_\tau\right).$$

Since j, the period in which plant capacity is added,[1] is to be chosen so as to minimize the costs over the interval from i to k, we set:

$$c_{ik} = \min_{i+1 \leqslant j \leqslant k} c_{ik}^j.$$

An example:

Suppose that the time horizon, demand increments, and single period construction cost functions remain the same as in the previous numerical example. Let each of the penalty coefficients $p_t = 2 \cdot 0$. In order to compute a typical coefficient, say c_{25}, we would compare the total of construction and penalty costs for three alternative cases: $j = 3$, 4, and 5.

$$c_{25} = \min\ [c_{25}^3, c_{25}^4, c_{25}^5]$$
$$= \min\ [28 \cdot 8 + 0, 23 \cdot 0 + 2 \cdot 0(1 \cdot 5), 18 \cdot 4 + 2 \cdot 0(1 \cdot 5) +$$
$$2 \cdot 0(3 \cdot 0)]$$
$$= 26 \cdot 0$$

and optimal $j = 4$.

In other words, if a point of regeneration were to occur at period 2 and the next one at period 5, the best policy for this interval would consist of building a single plant at period 4 and incurring $26 \cdot 0$ units of cost. The gains of deferring the investment from period 3 to 4

---

[1] Here the time index j plays a role similar to the decision variable y in the continuous time models of chapters 2 and 10 above. Both indicate how long to wait before constructing a new plant. Note, however, that y is defined as the time elapsing since the last previous point of regeneration, but that j is the number of periods elapsing since the first point of regeneration at time 0.

would outweigh the temporary import penalties on the $1 \cdot 5$ units of demand increment at period 3. Note that regardless of whether the plant is built at period 3, 4 or 5, its size would have to be $D_3 + D_4 + D_5 = 4 \cdot 0$ units of capacity. This size is implied by the initial assumption that periods 2 and 5 are both points of zero excess capacity.

Now that c_{ik} has been calculated, we know the minimum cost of moving from a regeneration point at i to the next regeneration point at k. The entire matrix of coefficients c_{ik} may be derived in a similar fashion. The dynamic programming recursion (11.10) may then be applied to determine a set of optimal regeneration points just as in the zero import case. Thus the computations for the case of temporary imports differ from those for no temporary imports only in the initial derivation of the c_{ik} cost coefficients. To allow for temporary imports, we do an optimization nested within another optimization.

REFERENCES

Bellman, R., and S. Dreyfus, *Applied Dynamic Programming*, Princeton University Press, Princeton, N. J., 1962.

Charnes, A., and W. W. Cooper, *Management Models and Industrial Applications of Linear Programming*, Vol. I, John Wiley and Sons, New York, 1961.

Hadley, G., *Linear Algebra*, Addison Wesley, Reading, Massachusetts, 1961.

Hadley, G., *Nonlinear and Dynamic Programming*, Addison Wesley, Reading, Massachusetts, 1964.

Manne, A. S., 'Programming of Economic Lot Sizes', *Management Science*, January 1958.

Veinott, A. F. Jr., 'Production Planning with Concave Costs', unpublished class notes, Stanford University, Stanford, California, 1963.

Wagner, H. M., and T. M. Whitin, 'Dynamic Version of the Economic Lot Size Model', *Management Science*, October 1958. (See also H. M. Wagner and T. M. Whitin, 'Dynamic Problems in the Theory of the Firm', Appendix 6 of T. M. Whitin, *Theory of Inventory Management*, 2nd ed., Princeton University Press, Princeton, N. J., 1957.)

Wagner, H. M., 'A Postscript to "Dynamic Problems in the Theory of the Firm",' *Naval Research Logistics Quarterly*, March 1960.

Zangwill, W. I., 'A Dynamic Multi-Product Multi-Facility Production and Inventory Model', Technical Report No. 1, Program in Operations Research, Stanford University, Stanford, California, April 1965.

PART III

MULTIPLE PRODUCING AREAS—
FURTHER RESULTS

CHAPTER 12

TWO PRODUCING AREAS—
CONSTANT CYCLE TIME POLICIES

ALAN S. MANNE[1]

The constant cycle length restriction

Both this chapter and the following ones deal with computational techniques for the case of multiple producing areas. The principal objective here is to develop a heuristic algorithm superior to the single- and two-phase models described and applied in Part I of this volume. We shall be particularly concerned with whether such an improved algorithm significantly alters any of the policy conclusions on plant size in the Indian case studies. Before proceeding to these more realistic applications with up to 15 producing areas, we shall examine more closely the case of two producing areas. In this comparatively simple situation, heuristic methods can be checked directly against dynamic programming solutions.

The principle underlying the heuristic computations is that constant cycle time policies are the only class of plant construction sequences to be considered. With this restriction, an integer programming model is formulated—one that may be solved exactly through enumeration for the two-region case and one that may be solved through approximate methods when there are more than two producing regions.

By a constant cycle time policy for producing region i, we mean that there are only two decision variables to be chosen: y_i (the onstream date for the first plant to be built in that region) and x_i (the length of time elapsing between the onstream dates of the first and the second unit).[2] The more distant future is idealized as though the nth plant will be brought onstream at time $y_i + x_i (n - 1)$. Unlike the single-phase policies described in Part I, there is no requirement that the onstream dates in producing regions i and j be identical. Moreover, unlike two-phase policies, the cycle time in region i is not

---

[1] The author is indebted to Donald Erlenkotter for helpful comments and for assistance with the numerical analysis.

[2] For a preinvestment survey, what really matters is the size, location and time-phasing of the *next* project to be built. By restricting the analysis to the two decision variables x_i and y_i, the more distant future is idealized in an aggregative way.

necessarily identical with that in j. In short, there is no requirement that $x_i = x_j$, or that $y_i = y_j$.

It has already been noted that constant cycle time policies are optimal for the case of a *single* producing area with demands growing arithmetically over time, with a constant construction cost function, a constant import penalty cost function, a constant discount rate, an infinite plant life, and an infinite time horizon.[1] Constant cycle time policies are not necessarily optimal when there are multiple producing areas.

An integer programming formulation for an infinite time horizon

If constant cycle time policies are to be followed over an infinite time horizon, an integer programming model of size, location and time-phasing can be formulated along the following lines: (1) demands in the vicinity of producing area i are growing at the constant annual arithmetic rate of D_i, (2) the discount rate, construction costs, and penalty costs for inter-regional transport remain constant over the indefinite future, (3) the plant life is infinite, (4) excess capacities are exactly zero in each region at time zero, (5) time is idealized in discrete periods, e.g. a single year in length, and (6) excess capacities are to return to zero every T periods, where T is an arbitrarily specified length of time. Note that the first four of these assumptions are identical with those employed throughout Part I and also in Chapter 10 of this volume. Assumption (5) (discrete time) is utilized here so that the construction and transport costs may be calculated at a finite number of points in time—hence through a finite number of variables in the integer programming formulation.

The motivation for assumption (6) is this: It permits us to do our cost calculations as though the time horizon were infinite and as though demands were expanding arithmetically over the indefinite future.[2] By postulating that there is to be a return to zero excess capacity (a point of regeneration) every T periods, we ensure that the

[1] In chapter 9, T. N. Srinivasan showed that constant cycle time policies are also optimal for the case of a single producing region with demands growing *geometrically* over time, with a constant exponent construction cost function, zero imports, a constant discount rate, an infinite plant life, and an infinite time horizon.

[2] Assumptions (4) and (6) comprise a set of initial and terminal conditions that seem appropriate for the Indian industries studied. An altogether different set of assumptions would be required to idealize a situation in which there is already a considerable volume of plant capacity in existence. The initial situation would *not* be a regeneration point (zero excess capacity at all potential producing locations), and there would be no reason to expect that it would be a desirable policy to repeat the initial configuration of excess capacities every T units of time over the indefinite future.

events at each point of time—the size of plants brought onstream and the physical quantities shipped from one area to another—will be repeated every T periods. It is for this reason that we refer to the arbitrary integer T as the length of a 'major cycle'. During the course of such a cycle, region i will have its own minor cycles of plant construction—each one x_i time periods in length. In order that excess capacity return to zero at the end of a major cycle, the cumulative capacity built must equal the increment in demand during that time. Letting v_i denote the physical size of unit constructed in region i, assumption (6) implies:

$$\begin{pmatrix} \text{number of plants} \\ \text{built during} \\ \text{a major cycle} \end{pmatrix} \cdot \begin{pmatrix} \text{size of} \\ \text{each} \\ \text{plant built} \end{pmatrix} = \begin{matrix} \text{demand increment over a} \\ \text{major cycle} \end{matrix}$$

$$\left(\frac{T}{x_i}\right) \cdot (v_i) = TD_i$$

$$\therefore v_i = x_i D_i \quad \dots \dots \quad (12.1)$$

$$\text{and} \quad T/x_i = \text{a positive integer} \quad (12.2)$$

The quotient T/x_i represents the number of plants built during a major cycle. In order for the construction sequences within each major cycle to be identical with those of its predecessor, the number of plants built must be a positive integer. This is why condition (12.2) restricts the minor cycle length x_i to those values which will be consistent with a positive integer value for the quotient T/x_i. E.g. if $T = 24$ periods, it would not be possible to choose either 5 or 10 periods as the minor cycle length. The only admissible values of x_i would be: 1, 2, 3, 4, 6, 8, 12 and 24 periods.

In selecting y_i (the first onstream date), we restrict the choice to non-negative integer values satisfying (12.3). If (12.3) were violated, there would be fewer than T/x_i plants built prior to the date T:

$$y_i < x_i \quad \dots \dots \quad (12.3)$$

Unknowns and constraints in the integer programming formulation

The mixed integer programming formulation operates in terms of zero-one variables δ_{ik} to select one or another plant construction sequence k for producing region i. The kth sequence for region i is in turn defined through a pair of integers: x_i, the minor cycle length, and y_i, the first onstream date.

Example: If $T = 4$ periods, restriction (12.2) implies that the following values for x_i are admissible: 1, 2 or 4 periods. There will then be exactly 7 construction sequences that satisfy (12.2) and (12.3). Table 12.1 enumerates these seven possible alternative sequences of installed capacity.[1] E.g. when the sequence index $k = 3$, this identifies the case in which $x_i = 2$ and $y_i = 1$. Sequence 3 identifies that plan in which, starting with onstream date 1, a unit is to be built every other period to cover exactly two periods' worth of demand increment in region i. Throughout the period ending at date 1, 2, 3 and 4, the installed capacity available would be respectively: 0, $2D_i$, $2D_i$, and $4D_i$.

TABLE 12.1

Alternative sequences of installed capacity
(major cycle length $T = 4$)

Sequence index k		1	2	3	4	5	6	7
Minor cycle length, x_i		1	2	2	4	4	4	4
First onstream date, y_i		0	0	1	0	1	2	3
b_k^t, installed capacity available through-out period ending at date t; multiples of single-period demand increment D_i	$t = 1$	1	2	0	4	0	0	0
	$t = 2$	2	2	2	4	4	0	0
	$t = 3$	3	4	2	4	4	4	0
	$t = 4 = T$	4	4	4	4	4	4	4

For short, we shall hereafter use the symbol b_k^t to denote the quantity by which the single-period demand increment must be multiplied in order to arrive at the installed capacity available

---

[1] In order to increase computational efficiency, the individual sequences need not be generated all at once, but instead might be generated one-at-a-time as suggested in a similar context by Gilmore and Gomory (1961). As the major cycle length T increases, the number of possible alternate sequences is approximately $2T$. The exact numbers are as follows:

Major cycle length, T	Number of possible alternative sequences
4 periods	7 sequences
8 ,,	15 ,,
12 ,,	28 ,,
16 ,,	31 ,,
20 ,,	42 ,,
24 ,,	60 ,,
30 ,,	72 ,,
32 ,,	63 ,,

throughout the period ending at date t if the kth construction sequence is employed. E.g. the vector $(b_3^1, b_3^2, b_3^3, b_3^4) = (0, 2, 2, 4)$. Note that the multiplier b_k^T is identically equal to T. Restrictions (12.1)–(12.3) ensure that the sequences will all be constructed so that a point of regeneration (zero excess capacity in each producing region) is reached every T periods.

The mixed integer programme consists of assigning values to the zero-one variables δ_{ik} and to the continuous variables s_{ij}^t. The latter indicate how large a quantity is to be shipped out of producing area i into area j during period t. The two sets of unknowns are to be chosen subject to the peak demand constraints (12.4), the average demand constraints (12.5), the zero-one constraints (12.6), and the non-negativity restraints (12.7):

| Capacity available throughout all areas during period t | $\geqslant$ Peak demand facing all areas at end of period t |

$$\sum_i \sum_k (b_k^t D_i)\, \delta_{ik} \qquad\qquad \geqslant t \sum_i D_i$$

$$(t = 1, 2, \ldots T) \quad . \quad (12.4)$$

| Capacity available in area i during period t | + Incoming shipments to area i | − Outgoing shipments from area i | $\geqslant$ Average demand facing area i during period t |

$$\sum_k (b_k^t D_i)\, \delta_{ik} + \sum_{j \neq i} s_{ji}^t \qquad - \sum_{j \neq i} s_{ij}^t \qquad \geqslant (t - 1/2)D_i$$

$$\text{(all } i, t) \quad . \quad . \quad . \quad . \quad (12.5)$$

$$\sum_k \delta_{ik} = 1 \quad \text{(all } i) \quad . \quad . \quad . \quad . \quad . \quad (12.6)$$

$$s_{ij}^t \geqslant 0 \quad \text{(all } i, j, t) \quad . \quad . \quad . \quad . \quad (12.7)$$

Restrictions (12.4) and (12.5) are designed so that the numerical results of this discrete time formulation will be roughly comparable with those obtained from the continuous time models described in Part I of this volume. In those continuous time models, it was supposed that the demands facing producing area i at time t were tD_i, with t a non-negative real number—but not necessarily an integer. Restrictions (12.4) guarantee that the construction sequence variables δ_{ik} will be chosen so that there will always be enough capacity available throughout the system for meeting the *peak* demands occurring at the end of each period.

Restrictions (12.5) ensure that the shipment variables s_{ij}^t are chosen so as to meet the *average* demands facing area i during period t. E.g. a continuous time model would imply satisfying a demand of zero at the beginning of the first period and D_i at the end of that period. Instead, constraints (12.5) ensure that the activity levels will satisfy the average demand rates during that first period, namely $(1/2)D_i$.

The activity levels are to be chosen so as to minimize the total of construction and shipping costs discounted over an infinite time horizon. Expressions for the individual cost coefficients are shown in (12.8) and (12.9) below.[1] The zero-one unknown δ_{ik} has a cost coefficient which may be calculated from the cycle length x_i and the first onstream date y_i:

Plant size in region i $\qquad = v_i = x_i D_i$

Cost of a single plant of size v_i $= f(v_i)$

Discounted cost of an infinite
sequence of plants built every $= \dfrac{f(v_i)}{1 - e^{-rx_i}}$
x_i periods starting at time zero

Discounted cost of an infinite
sequence of plants built every
x_i periods starting at date y_i; $= (e^{-ry_i} \cdot) \dfrac{f(v_i)}{1 - e^{-rx_i}}$ $\quad \cdot \quad$ (12.8)
cost coefficient for unknown
δ_{ik}

The continuous unknowns s_{ij}^t have cost coefficients which may be determined as follows from the single period penalty coefficients p_{ij}:

Proportional penalty cost per
unit manufactured at produc- $= p_{ij}$
ing area i and shipped to
market area j[2]

---

[1] (12.8) is designed to cover the case where each capacity increment is obtained through a balanced plant built at a single point of time. The cost of new capacity is then independent of the existing equipment already installed in that producing area. In order to cover more complex situations (e.g. an alternation between 'new units' and 'substantial expansions' as in the Indian cement industry, chapter 6 above), expression (12.8) must be modified.

[2] The coefficient p_{ij} includes only the *excess* over those proportional costs required for area j to supply itself. From this definition, $p_{jj} = 0$, and $p_{ij} \geqslant 0$.

Discounted penalty cost per
unit shipped during period t;
calculated as though shipments
take place at a steady rate from $= \int_{\tau=t-1}^{t} p_{ij} e^{-r\tau} \, d\tau$
the beginning to the end of
period t; discount rate $r =$
10% per period

$$= 1 \cdot 05 \, e^{-t/10} \, p_{ij}$$

Discounted penalty cost of an
infinite sequence of one unit $= \dfrac{1 \cdot 05 \, e^{-t/10} \, p_{ij}}{1 - e^{-T/10}}$ . . . (12.9)
shipped every T periods start-
ing with period t; cost coefficient for unknown s_{ij}^t

Table 12.2 illustrates a tableau of non-zero coefficients for the two-region mixed integer programming model when T = 4. For concreteness, the following values are assigned to the demand increments in regions 1 and 2: $D_1 = 1 \cdot 0$ and $D_2 = 0 \cdot 5$. The single-period discount rate $r = 0 \cdot 10$. Specific numerical values are not shown, however, for the construction cost functions $f(v_i)$ or for the penalty coefficients p_{ij}.

Both from Table 12.2, as well as from the original problem statement contained in expressions (12.4)–(12.9), it will be observed that this problem is decomposable into T independent single-period 'transportation' sub-problems. That is, once numerical values are assigned to the zero-one unknowns δ_{ik}, there remain only T independent linear programming calculations of the 'transportation' type—each involving one or another set of the variables s_{ij}^t.[1] This decomposable structure can be exploited to provide a significant increase in the efficiency of numerical analysis.

Effect of major cycle length

The greater the length of each major cycle T, the more opportunity there will be for alternate plant sizes and onstream dates—hence the greater the likelihood of lowering the total costs discounted over an infinite horizon. However, the greater the value of T, the more expensive becomes the task of numerical analysis. In order to check the effect of this rather arbitrary parameter, we will now present some integer programming numerical results for the two-region case.

---

[1] Rosen and Ornea (1963) would refer to the δ_{ik} as 'coupling' variables. Once that zero-one values are assigned to these variables, the overall problem is decomposable into two or more independent linear programming subproblems.

TABLE 12.2

Tableau of non-zero coefficients for two-region integer programming model
($T = 4$, $D_1 = 1·0$, $D_2 = 0·5$, $r = 0·10$)

	(Zero-one variables)														(Non-negative variables)								Right-hand side constants	Constraint identification
	δ_{1k}							δ_{2k}							s^1_{ij}		s^2_{ij}		s^3_{ij}		s^4_{ij}			
	$k=1$	2	3	4	5	6	7	$k=1$	2	3	4	5	6	7	$i,j=2,1$	1,2	2,1	1,2	2,1	1,2	2,1	1,2		
Peak demand constraints (12.4)	1	2			4			0·5	1			2											≥ 1·50	$t=1$
	2	2	2		4			1·0	1	1		2	2										≥ 3·00	$t=2$
	3	4	2		4	4		1·5	2	1	2		2	2									≥ 4·50	$t=3$
	4	4	4	4	4			2·0	2	2	2	2	2	2									≥ 6·00	$t=4$
Average demand constraints (12.5)	1	2			4										−1								≥ 0·50	$j=1\}\,t=1$
								0·5	1			2				−1							≥ 0·25	$j=2\}\,t=1$
	2	2	2		4												−1						≥ 1·50	$j=1\}\,t=2$
								1·0	1	1		2	2					−1					≥ 0·75	$j=2\}\,t=2$
	3	4	2		4	4													−1				≥ 2·50	$j=1\}\,t=3$
								1·5	2	1	2		2	2						−1			≥ 1·25	$j=2\}\,t=3$
	4	4	4	4	4																−1		≥ 3·50	$j=1\}\,t=4$
								2·0	2	2	2	2	2	2								−1	≥ 1·75	$j=2\}\,t=4$
Zero-one constraints (12.6)	1	1	1	1	1	1	1																= 1·0	$i=1$
								1	1	1	1	1	1	1									= 1·0	$i=2$
Cost coefficients from (12.8) and (12.9)	10·5 $f(1·0)$	5·5 $f(2·0)$	5·0 $f(2·0)$	3·0 $f(4·0)$	2·7 $f(4·0)$	2·5 $f(4·0)$	2·2 $f(4·0)$	10·5 $f(0·5)$	5·5 $f(1·0)$	5·0 $f(1·0)$	3·0 $f(2·0)$	2·7 $f(2·0)$	2·5 $f(2·0)$	2·2 $f(2·0)$	2·9 p_{21}	2·9 p_{12}	2·6 p_{21}	2·6 p_{12}	2·4 p_{21}	2·4 p_{12}	2·1 p_{21}	2·1 p_{12}		

Idealizing time in discrete units of a single year, the following are plausible alternate lengths for a major cycle: $T = 12$, 16, 20 and 24 years. Throughout, the economies-of-scale parameter and the discount rate are fixed at the following typical values: $a = 0 \cdot 70$ and $r = 0 \cdot 10$/year.

The more rapidly growing region is identified as area 1, and physical units are normalized so that the annual increment of demand in this region is $D_1 = 1 \cdot 0$. The annual demand increment in the other region is taken as $D_2 = 0 \cdot 5$. (In a subsequent section, we consider an alternate value, $D_2 = 1 \cdot 0$.)

Construction costs are taken to be identical in the two producing regions, and are normalized so that the cost of building a single plant is $kv^a = v^{0 \cdot 7}$, where the physical size of unit built is v. The penalty cost for one unit of inter-regional shipments is p_{ij}, and for simplicity's sake we have made the symmetrical assumption that $p_{12} = p_{21}$.

In order to solve the two-region mixed integer programming model described in (12.4)–(12.9), a special-purpose enumerative routine was used.[1] This routine takes advantage of the restrictions that conditions (12.4) impose upon any combination of construction sequences. E.g. when $T = 24$, there are 60 possible sequences of plant construction to be considered for each region. This does not mean that $60^2 = 3,600$ combinations have to be examined for both regions together, but instead only the 238 combinations that satisfy the peak demand constraints (12.4).

The integer programming calculations are designed so as to investigate the combined effects of two parameters: T (the major cycle length) and p_{ij} (the unit penalty cost). Since p_{ij} enters as a multiplicative factor in the minimand, the total costs were tabulated separately for the construction and the penalty cost components, and only the 'efficient' combinations of these two components were retained. In this way, a single enumerative calculation provided the basic information needed for all alternative values of the penalty cost parameter p_{ij}.

Figure 12.1 summarizes the numerical results obtained in this way. As might have been anticipated, the total discounted costs increase with p_{ij}, but at a non-increasing rate. Somewhat less expected is the result that if p_{ij} is held constant, the total discounted costs do *not* change significantly with the major cycle lengths considered here.[2] On the basis of these numerical results, we have

[1] Donald Erlenkotter programmed this routine for use on the Stanford University I.B.M. 7090 computer.

[2] For these major cycle lengths, the greater the value of T, the more alternate plant sequencing possibilities are available. It might plausibly be conjectured that

concluded that there is little to be gained by considering major cycle lengths in excess of 24 years. This is the value of T employed in all subsequent numerical calculations.

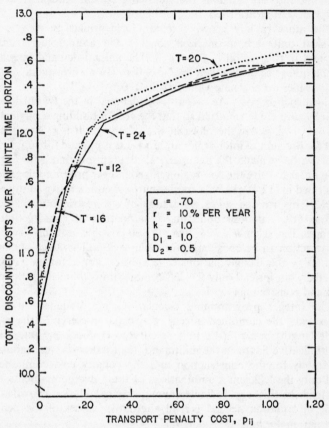

Figure 12.1.—Integer Programming Solutions For Two-Region Problem

Integer programming—optimal construction sequences

Underlying each of the cost curves in Figure 12.1 is an optimal set of plant construction sequences. Table 12.3 lists these sequences for the case of $T = 24$, and also shows the range of values of p_{ij} within

an increase in T will therefore lead to a decrease in the total costs discounted over an infinite horizon. There is an immediate counter-example to this conjecture in Figure 12.1. The rightmost segment of the cost curve for $T = 20$ lies above that for $T = 12$.

which each of these is optimal.[1] E.g. for $0.016 \leqslant p_{ij} \leqslant 0.122$, the optimal policy is described as $x_1 = 12$, $x_2 = 12$, $y_1 = 4$, $y_2 = 0$. This means that a minor cycle length of 12 years is to be utilized in both regions, that the first plant is to be onstream in region 2 at time zero, and the second is to be onstream in region 1 at time 4.

TABLE 12.3

Optimal plant construction sequences
($a = 0.70$, $r = 0.10$, $k = 1.0$, $D_1 = 1.0$, $D_2 = 0.5$, $T = 24$)

Range of values of p_{ij}	Optimal policy				Cost components for optimal policy		
	Minor cycle length (years)	First onstream date (years)			Invest-ment costs	Inter-regional transport penalties*	Total costs*
	x_1 x_2	y_1 y_2					
$0 \quad <p_{ij} \leqslant 0.016$	12 12	0	8		10.402	0	10.402
$0.016 < p_{ij} \leqslant 0.122$	12 12	4	0		10.478	0.137	10.615
$0.122 < p_{ij} \leqslant 0.287$	8 8	2	0		11.166	0.390	11.556
$0.287 < p_{ij} \leqslant 0.632$	8 8	1	0		11.837	0.244	12.081
$0.632 < p_{ij} \leqslant 1.050$	6 8	0	1		12.105	0.268	12.373
$1.050 < p_{ij} \leqslant \infty$	6 6	0	0		12.551	0	12.551

NOTE: * Interregional transport penalties when p_{ij} is at the lower end of the indicated range.

Note that the lower the import penalty p_{ij}, the longer become the optimal cycle times—hence the larger the plant sizes for the two producing regions. This result closely resembles that obtained in Chapter 10 for the case of a single producing region with unlimited import possibilities.

According to Table 12.3, it is not necessarily the more rapidly growing region that is the first one to build its plant. This all depends

[1] The lower the value of p_{ij}, the more advantageous it is to substitute inter-regional transport in place of investment costs for manufacturing plants. It is for this reason that the optimal level of the investment cost component drops with p_{ij}.

upon the numerical parameter values. For the lowest values of p_{ij}, it pays to build the first plant in region 1; for intermediate values in region 2; and for the highest values, it pays to start both plants simultaneously at time 0.

Table 12.3 provides one example in which it is optimal to employ a different minor cycle length for each region. Within the parameter range $0 \cdot 632 \leqslant p_{ij} \leqslant 1 \cdot 050$, it is optimal to set $x_1 = 6$ and $x_2 = 8$.

Integer programming—upper and lower bounds upon costs

Figure 12.2 reproduces the two-region integer programming cost curve for $T = 24$, and compares that curve with upper and lower

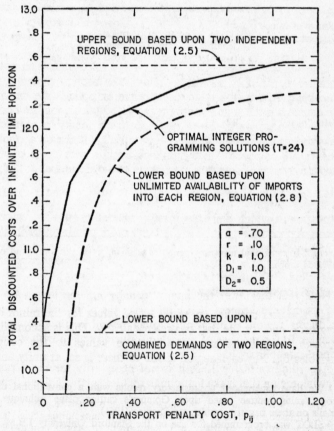

Figure 12.2.—Upper and Lower Bounds on Costs for Two-Region Problem

bounds derived from models of a single producing region. The *upper* bound is obtained by supposing that neither region is permitted to import from the other at any time. With this constraint, the problem is reduced to two independent single-region calculations of the type described in equation (2.5). Similarly, a *lower* bound is derived by supposing that each region is free to ship to the other at zero cost at all times. The situation is then equivalent to a case in which a single producing region is to supply the combined demands of regions 1 and 2, and may again be described by equation (2.5).

Another set of lower bounds is obtained by supposing that each region is free to import an *un*limited quantity from the other at a constant unit penalty cost p_{ij}. The situation is then equivalent to two independent regions, each employing time-phased imports as described by equation (2.8). For low values of p_{ij}, it is clear that this lower bound will not be a sharp one. However, for $p_{ij} \geqslant 0.12$, it turns out that this bound is uniformly higher than that based upon equation (2.5).

The two lower bounds shown in Figure 12.2 impose an outside limit upon the cost reduction obtainable through dynamic programming. Although dynamic programming policies are free from the constant cycle time restriction and although an infinite horizon model eliminates the arbitrary major cycle length parameter T, nevertheless the lower bounds of Figure 12.2 still remain applicable. Chapter 13 compares these numerical results with those obtained through dynamic programming for the two-region case.

A heuristic integer programming routine

For cases in which there are more than two producing regions, it becomes expensive to solve the integer programming model (12.4)–(12.9) by direct enumeration.[1] Instead a heuristic integer programming routine has been applied. For short, this computer programme is labelled SLOT (Size, LOcation and Time-phasing).[2]

SLOT operates as follows:

(1) The user specifies an initial set of values for the minor cycle lengths x_i and for the first onstream dates y_i. This is accomplished through assigning appropriate zero-one values to the coupling variables δ_{ik}. For each region i, one of these is set at unity and all

---

[1] We have experienced unsatisfactory results with a conventional integer programming routine based upon Gomory's cutting plane technique. For details on these negative results, see Shapiro (1965).

[2] SLOT was programmed for use on the Stanford University I.B.M. 7090 computer.

others at zero. The δ_{ik} may be chosen in any arbitrary way, provided that the peak demand constraints (12.4) are satisfied.

(2) Given the integer values of δ_{ik}, the plant construction costs are determined directly through the cost coefficients of (12.8). Inter-regional transport penalty costs are determined through solving a series of T independent 'transportation' problems[1] in terms of the inter-regional shipment variables s_{ij}^t.

(3) For purposes of local optimization, an arbitrary sequence of producing regions is specified.[2] That is, when region i is being examined, the programme determines minimum-cost values of the δ_{ik} variables for region i—given the setting of these decision variables in all other producing regions. (The programme automatically rejects any δ_{ik} values which would cause the peak demand condition (12.4) to be violated.) The costs of construction and of transport are again computed as in step 2.

(4) Given the locally optimal values of the δ_{ik} for region i, the programme then proceeds to examine the next region in the arbitrarily specified sequence. Again a local optimization is performed—holding fixed the values of the decision variables in all other producing regions. The procedure is repeated until there is no longer any decrease in overall costs obtainable by changing the δ_{ik} variables in a single region.

NOTE. This one-at-a-time heuristic procedure is not guaranteed to arrive at an optimal integer programming solution. There is considerable evidence, however, that such an algorithm will provide a reasonably satisfactory approximation. See Reiter and Sherman (1962) and Manne (1964).

Figure 12.3 provides some evidence on the magnitude of error produced by applying SLOT to the two-region numerical problem for which we already know the optimal integer programming solutions. An initial value of unity was assigned to the δ_{ik} variables so that $x_i = 12$, $y_i = 0$. The points marked with circles result from

[1] These 'transportation' subproblems could themselves be solved by linear programming, but in order to speed up the heuristic routine we have made use of a non-optimal procedure that Kuhn and Baumol (1962) have christened SMALC (Ship Most At Least Cost). They describe this procedure as follows: 'The basic idea is to find which route involves costs lower than any other and to ship as much as possible along this route. Then we ship as much as possible along the second-lowest cost route and so on, until all excesses have been eliminated and all requirements have been filled.' (ibid., p. 6). On the basis of the numerical results reported by Kuhn and Baumol, it is believed that SMALC will seldom lead to a major error in estimating the transport penalty costs.

[2] One convenient ordering of regions is to follow some such criterion as 'ascending order of the demand increments D_i'. Another alternative is to randomize the order in which the regions are to be examined.

applying SLOT so that all those decision variables for region 1 are examined first, then those for region 2, then those for region 1 again, etc. By reversing this order of local optimization, we obtain those points marked with triangles.

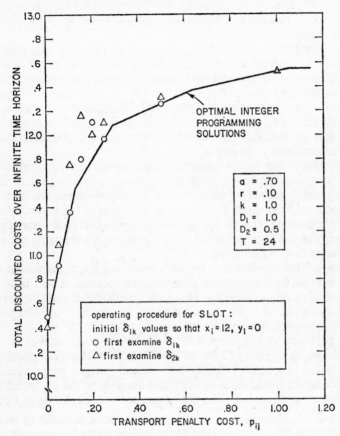

Figure 12.3.—Comparison of SLOT with Optimal Integer Programming Solutions

Results are shown for each of eight alternative values of the penalty parameter p_{ij}. In six of the eight cases, it turns out that one or the other ordering leads to an optimal integer programming solution. (Either a circle or a triangle lies on the minimum cost curve.) In the two remaining cases where $p_{ij} = 0 \cdot 15$ and $0 \cdot 20$, the error in costs is roughly 2%.

Similar results are shown in Figure 12.4 for a different numerical problem—one obtained by setting the parameter $D_2 = 1\cdot0$ and maintaining all other parameter values constant. Regions 1 and 2 are now completely symmetrical, and it makes no difference in

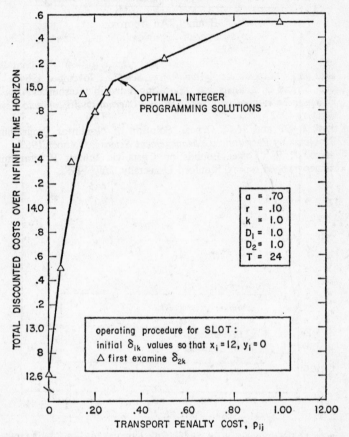

Figure 12.4.—Comparison of SLOT with Optimal Integer Programming Solutions

which order the regions are arranged for local optimization. Again SLOT arrived at an integer programming optimum in six out of eight cases, and there was a 2% error in costs for the remaining two.

REFERENCES

Gilmore, P. C., and R. E. Gomory, 'A Linear Programming to the Cutting-Stock Problem', *Operations Research*, November–December 1961.

Kuhn, H. W., and W. J. Baumol, 'An Approximative Algorithm for the Fixed-Charges Transportation Problem', *Naval Research Logistics Quarterly*, March 1962.

Manne, A. S., 'Plant Location under Economies-of-Scale—Decentralization and Computation', *Management Science*, November 1964.

Reiter, S., and G. R. Sherman, 'Allocating Indivisible Resources Affording External Economies or Diseconomies', *International Economic Review*, January 1962.

Rosen, J. B., and J. C. Ornea, 'Solution of Nonlinear Programming Problems by Partitioning', *Management Science*, October 1963.

Shapiro, J. F., 'Lower Bounds on Costs via Integer Programming', mimeographed report, Stanford University, July 1965.

O

CHAPTER 13

TWO PRODUCING AREAS— DYNAMIC PROGRAMMING SOLUTIONS

DONALD ERLENKOTTER[1]

This chapter applies the method of dynamic programming to find plant construction policies without the restriction of constant cycle length for the case of two producing areas. It is shown how a straightforward dynamic programming formulation can be simplified substantially by developing and using a combination of some necessary properties of an optimal solution and plausible restrictions on the structure of the solution. In effect, the two-area problem is reduced to one involving a single-dimensional state variable and a single-dimensional decision variable. In current research, an attempt is being made to find conditions and rigorous proofs that the restrictions made on the structure of the solution are in fact properties of an optimal solution.

The modified dynamic programming formulation has been solved using a standard linear programming code. The results obtained are compared with the integer programming methods using the constant cycle length restriction described in Chapter 12 above. While the approach of dynamic programming may be extended conceptually to include problems of many producing areas, the rapid growth in computational time required with the addition of each new area would seem to limit practical application of the method (at least with the computing restrictions of equipment available in the mid-1960s) to problems involving at most four areas.

A straightforward dynamic programming formulation

The following assumptions will be common to the formulations in this chapter: (1) demand in producing area i is growing at the constant annual arithmetic rate D_i, (2) the discount rate r, plant investment cost function $f_i(x_i D_i)$ for a plant of size $x_i D_i$ in area i, and penalty rates p_{ij} for manufacturing one unit at i and shipping

[1] The author is indebted to Alan S. Manne for helpful comments. This study was made under a fellowship granted by the Richard D. Irwin Foundation. The conclusions, opinions, and other statements in this paper, however, are the sole responsibility of the author.

it to j remain stationary over the indefinite future, (3) the plant life is infinite, and (4) total discounted costs of plant investment and inter-regional transport penalties are to be minimized over an infinite time horizon subject to the constraint that overall excess capacity for both areas be non-negative. If we let the excess capacity (measured in years of demand growth)[1] in producing area i be y_i, the constraint of (4) becomes:

$$(y_1 D_1) + (y_2 D_2) \geqslant 0 \quad . \quad . \quad . \quad . \quad . \quad (13.1)$$

at every instant in time t.

A dynamic programming formulation of this problem is straight-forward if we let y_1 and y_2 be the state variables and x_1 and x_2 be the decision variables. If $C(y_1, y_2)$ is the discounted cost for an optimal policy starting with resource combination (y_1, y_2), the quantity shipped from area i to area j at time t after construction of a plant of size x_j is $s_{ij}(t) = \max\{0, -(D_j)(y_j(t) + x_j)\}$, and plants may be constructed only at discrete time intervals of length ϵ, a solution is obtained by solving the functional equation:

$$C(y_1, y_2) = \min_{x_1 x_2 \geqslant 0} \left\{ \begin{array}{l} \text{immediate} \\ \text{plant} \\ \text{investment} \\ \text{costs} \end{array} + \begin{array}{l} \text{shipping} \\ \text{costs} \\ \text{during} \\ \text{the} \\ \text{interval} \\ \text{of length} \\ \epsilon \end{array} + \begin{array}{l} \text{discounted} \\ \text{future cost} \\ \text{with the} \\ \text{resource} \\ \text{combina-} \\ \text{tion at the} \\ \text{end of the} \\ \text{time} \\ \text{interval } \epsilon \end{array} \right\}$$

$$= \min_{x_1, x_2 \geqslant 0} \left\{ \sum_{i=1}^{2} f_i(x_i D_i) + \sum_{\substack{j=1 \\ (i=1,2 \\ i \neq j)}}^{2} \left[\int_0^\epsilon p_{ij} s_{ij}(t) e^{-rt} dt \right] \right.$$

$$\left. + e^{-r\epsilon} C(y_1 + x_1 - \epsilon, y_2 + x_2 - \epsilon) \right\}$$

where the minimum is taken subject to

$$(y_1 + x_1 - \epsilon)D_1 + (y_2 + x_2 - \epsilon)D_2 \geqslant 0$$

Note that unlike the procedures of Chapter 12 above, this method will provide the costs and policies for any initial combination of

---

[1] Manipulation of this particular model seems easier if excess capacity is measured in years of demand growth rather than in physical units.

excess capacities (y_1, y_2)—not only those for the point of regeneration $(0, 0)$. This functional equation may be solved by the methods of successive approximations or approximation in policy space (see Bellman (1957) or Bellman and Dreyfus (1962)). Since we have two state variables and two decision variables, these computations will be lengthy even on a computer of the type available during the 1960s. If each y_i takes integer values between $+15$ and -15, we would have to consider roughly 450 feasible state combinations. If we also consider 15 values for each x_i, up to 225 decision possibilities may be made from each state combination and the number of state-decision combinations approaches 100,000. Considering a third producing area would add a state variable and a decision variable, and the computational burden would become unmanageable. If the $f_i(\cdot)$ are concave, some simplification might be obtained by methods similar to those of Zangwill (1965); however, his approach requires a finite horizon and is intended for the more general case of arbitrarily increasing demand. In the following sections the structure of the problem will be exploited to reduce its dimensionality and obtain a solution method in continuous time, free of arbitrary selection of a discrete time interval.

The structure of an optimal policy

As we try to determine the structure of an optimal policy, it will be helpful to visualize the two producing area problem in the form of its state-space diagram, Figure 13.1. If no plants are constructed, excess capacities in both areas will diminish over time along a 45-degree line determined by the initial excess capacity position. These lines will be called *excess capacity paths*, and will be identified by $P(y_1^0, y_2^0)$, where (y_1^0, y_2^0) is the point at which the path leaves the non-negative quadrant; thus we always have $y_1^0 \cdot y_2^0 = 0$. The decision to build a plant in one area causes a transition from one excess capacity path $P(y_1^0, y_2^0)$ to some other path $P(y_1^{0'}, y_2^{0'})$. If a plant of size $x_i D_i$ is built in area i, the identification of the new path $P(y_1^{0'}, y_2^{0'})$ is given by $y_i^{0'} = \max\{0, (x_i + y_i^0 - y_j^0)\}$ and $y_j^{0'} = \max\{0, -(x_i + y_i^0 - y_j^0)\}$. E.g. on Figure 13.1 a plant of size $x_1 D_1 = 7D_1$ causes a transition from $P(0, 4)$ to $P(3, 0)$.

The most apparent property of an optimal policy is that if excess capacity exists in both areas, it is not optimal to build a plant in either area. The plant could be delayed with no additional cost, and the discounted cost of its construction would decrease. So for an optimal policy decision (x_1^*, x_2^*) from (y_1, y_2), we write:

$$(y_1, y_2) > 0 \Rightarrow (x_1^*, x_2^*) = 0 \quad \ldots \quad (13.2)$$

On Figure 13.1, from any point in the non-negative quadrant, the initial excess capacity path $P(y_1^0, y_2^0)$ will be followed down at least as far as an axis.

Secondly, we see that if excess capacity exists in one area, it is not optimal to build a plant in that area unless the combined excess capacity of both areas is zero. As before, the plant can be delayed with a positive saving on its discounted investment costs and no increase in penalty shipment costs; hence:

$$y_i > 0 \text{ and } (y_1 D_1) + (y_2 D_2) > 0 \Rightarrow x_i^* = 0 \quad . \quad . \quad . \quad (13.3)$$

An excess capacity path will be followed down to the constraint line (13.1) unless a plant is constructed in the area which has a deficit in excess capacity.

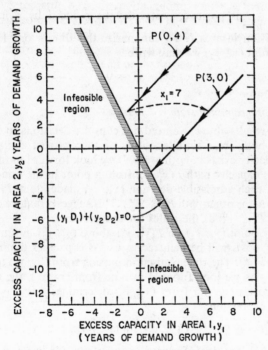

Figure 13.1.—State-Space Diagram for the Two Producing Area Problem

A third property of an optimal policy is that if penalty costs are finite, it is not optimal to build plants simultaneously in both areas. This is easily seen in cases not covered by (13.2) or (13.3) since building a plant in the area with no excess capacity creates precisely those situations, and immediate construction of a plant in the other area cannot be optimal. This argument is *not* valid for the case of $(y_1, y_2) = (0, 0)$. Instead, the following reasoning may be applied. The cost saving ΔC gained by delaying one plant decision a short interval of time ϵ and incurring a penalty cost for supplying demand from the area in which a plant is constructed immediately is:

$$\Delta C = f_i(x_i D_i) - \left[e^{-r\epsilon} f_i(x_i D_i) + \int_0^\epsilon p_{ji}(t D_i) e^{-rt} dt \right]$$

Assuming that p_{ji} is finite,

$$\frac{\partial \Delta C}{\partial \epsilon} = e^{-r\epsilon}[r f_i(x_i D_i) - p_{ji} \epsilon D_i]$$

Since $\dfrac{\partial \Delta C}{\partial \epsilon}\bigg|_{\epsilon=0}$ is positive, costs may be reduced by delaying the plant decision in area i. To summarize this discussion: From any feasible point $(y_{\ast}, y_2)$ we may write:

$$x_1^* \cdot x_2^* = 0 \qquad \cdots \cdots \cdots (13.4)$$

Dynamic programming state redefinition

From the results above, we need not consider decisions to construct plants in both areas simultaneously or to construct a plant when excess capacity exists in both areas. If we look forward in time along any excess capacity path $P(y_1^0, y_2^0)$ from a point in the non-negative quadrant, each admissible decision (x_1, x_2) made along $P(y_1^0, y_2^0)$ is a move to some other path $P(y_1^{0\prime}, y_2^{0\prime})$. This suggests that we designate the paths $P(y_1^0, y_2^0)$ as the states for this problem.

For any point (y_1, y_2) on $P(y_1^0, y_2^0)$ above (y_1^0, y_2^0), no investment or penalty costs will be incurred as excess capacities diminish over time to (y_1^0, y_2^0). The time elapsed in passing from (y_1, y_2) to (y_1^0, y_2^0) is $y_i - y_i^0$. As we look forward in time from (y_1, y_2), the total discounted cost $C(y_1^0, y_2^0)$ from (y_1^0, y_2^0) determines $C(y_1, y_2)$ by the following expression:

$$C(y_1, y_2) = e^{-r(y_i - y_i^0)} C(y_1^0, y_2^0) \text{ for } (y_1, y_2) \geqslant (y_1^0, y_2^0) \quad \cdots (13.5)$$

Similarly, we may look forward in time from (y_1^0, y_2^0) and write an expression relating $C(y_1^0, y_2^0)$ to the cost $C(y_1, y_2)$ for points (y_1, y_2) on $P(y_1^0, y_2^0)$ below (y_1^0, y_2^0) and before the point where the next plant is constructed, taking into account the transport penalties for supplying the capacity deficit in area i (i is identified by $y_i^0 = \min\{y_1^0, y_2^0\} \equiv 0$):

$$C(y_1^0, y_2^0) = \int_0^{y_i^0 - y_i} p_{ji}(tD_i) e^{-rt} dt + e^{-r(y_i^0 - y_i)} C(y_1, y_2) \quad . \quad . \quad (13.6)$$

$$\text{for } (y_1, y_2) \leqslant (y_1^0, y_2^0)$$

Since knowledge of the cost for proceeding from (y_1^0, y_2^0) may be inserted into (13.5) or (13.6) to determine the costs from other points on $P(y_1^0, y_2^0)$ before the next plant is constructed, we define $C(y_1^0, y_2^0)$ as the cost associated with being in state $P(y_1^0, y_2^0)$. Once the cost $C(y_1^0, y_2^0)$ has been determined, the costs from other initial excess capacity combinations along the path $P(y_1^0, y_2^0)$ can be computed as needed.

The regeneration point restriction

To further simplify the computation of a plant construction strategy, the following restriction will be made on the form of policies to be considered:

$$0 \geqslant y_i(x_i) \geqslant -x_i \quad . \quad . \quad . \quad . \quad . \quad (13.7)$$

where $y_i(x_i)$ is the excess capacity in area i when a plant of size x_i is constructed. Restriction (13.7) has two consequences: first, plants will be constructed only in an area where the excess capacity is non-positive; and second, the capacity constructed will at least wipe out the outstanding capacity deficit. This condition is named the *regeneration point restriction* because of its similarity to the regeneration point theorem proved in Chapter 10 for the single area problem with unlimited availability of imports.[1] Here, however, a general proof has not been found to show that the restriction is in fact a property of an optimal solution.

Another condition that $y_i(x_i)$ must satisfy is the feasibility constraint (13.1). For feasibility, we must have:

$$y_i(x_i) \geqslant -\frac{y_j^0 D_j}{D_1 + D_2}$$

Combining this with (13.7), the final restriction on the plant construction timing decision is:

$$0 \geqslant y_i(x_i) \geqslant \max \left\{ -x_i, -\frac{y_j^0 D_j}{D_1 + D_2} \right\} \quad . \quad . \quad (13.8)$$

---

[1] The single producing area plant size model with unlimited availability of imports is, of course, a special case of this two producing area model in which $y_j^0 = +\infty$. The sign convention used here for the y_1 is the negative of that used in Chapter 10, in which y represents the duration of the temporary import phase.

The dynamic programming reformulation

To reformulate the dynamic programming version of the problem with the excess capacity paths $P(y_1^0, y_2^0)$ defined as states, a functional equation is written relating the cost from each point (y_1^0, y_2^0) to any possible transition point $(y_1^{0'}, y_2^{0'})$ which may be reached by a plant construction decision. For construction decision x_i, the time elapsed in passing from (y_1^0, y_2^0) to $(y_1^{0'}, y_2^{0'})$ will be $\min\{x_i, y_j^0\}$. We can write:

$$C(y_1^0, y_2^0) = \min_{x_i, y_i} \left\{ \begin{array}{l} \text{transport} \\ \text{penalty} \\ \text{costs before} \\ \text{a plant is} \\ \text{constructed} \end{array} + \begin{array}{l} \text{discounted} \\ \text{plant in-} \\ \text{vestment} \\ \text{costs} \end{array} + \begin{array}{l} \text{discounted} \\ \text{future costs} \\ \text{starting} \\ \text{from the} \\ \text{resource} \\ \text{combination} \\ \text{designated} \\ \text{by the} \\ \text{transition} \\ \text{state path} \end{array} \right\}$$

$$= \min_{x_i, y_i} \left\{ \int_0^{-y_i} p_{ji}(tD_i) \, e^{-rt} \, dt + e^{ry_i} f_i(x_i D_i) \right.$$
$$\left. + e^{-r \min\{x_i, y_j^0\}} C(y_1^{0'}, y_2^{0'}) \right\} \quad . \quad . \quad (13.9)$$

where the choice of x_i and y_i is restricted by (13.8).

This formulation may be simplified further since a preliminary step will determine the minimizing value of y_i for any given choice of x_i. Fixing x_i and differentiating the expression in brackets in (13.9), we have:

$$\frac{\partial\{\ \}}{\partial y_i} = e^{ry_i} \{p_{ji} y_i D_i + rf_i(x_i D_i)\}$$

Note that $\dfrac{\partial\{\ \}}{\partial y_i} \gtrless 0$ as $y_i \gtrless -\dfrac{rf_i(x_i D_i)}{p_{ji}D_i}$. For given x_i, the minimizing value $y_i(x_i)$ taking into account the constraint (13.8) is:

$$y_i(x_i) = \max \left\{ -x_i, -\frac{y_j^0 D_j}{D_1 + D_2}, -\frac{rf_i(x_i D_i)}{p_{ji}D_i} \right\} \quad (13.10)$$

Substituting the result (13.10) into (13.9) gives the simplified dynamic programming functional relationship:

$$C(y_1^0, y_2^0) = \min_{x_i} \left\{ \int_0^{-y_i(x_i)} p_{ji}(tD_i) \, e^{-rt} \, dt + e^{ry_i(x_i)} f_i(x_i D_i) \right.$$
$$\left. + e^{-r \min \{x_i, y_j^0\}} C(y_1^{0'}, y_2^{0'}) \right\} \quad . \quad (13.11)$$

To solve (13.11) computationally, we assume some finite set of excess capacity paths as the state space. Then admissible plant decisions are those which will cause a transition from one path in the state space to another, e.g. if the y_i^0 are integer-valued, the admissible x_i must also be integer-valued. Note that in this formulation, with integer values for y_i^0 between $+15$ and -15 and x_i between 0 and $+15$, there are only 31 points in the state space with 30 decisions from point $(0, 0)$ and 15 from each other to consider. A substantial saving in dimensionality has been achieved over the earlier straightforward formulation. In addition, the need for specifying an arbitrary discrete time interval has been eliminated.

The policy iteration approach of Howard (1960) could be used to compute solutions,[1] but to take advantage of available computer codes the linear programming formulation suggested by d'Epenoux (1963) has been applied.[2] To simplify the notation, we shall assume that each of the m excess capacity paths $P(y_1^0, y_2^0)$ is identified by an index h, and that an index k has been assigned to the n_h admissible plant decisions made from each excess capacity path. We then define:

$$\alpha_{h,k} = e^{-r \min \{x_i, y_j^0\}}$$

and

$$b_{h,k} = \int_0^{-y_i(x_i)} p_{ji}(tD_i) \, e^{-rt} \, dt + e^{ry_i(x_i)} f_i(x_i D_i)$$

The linear programming formulation is obtained by rewriting (13.11) as a set of inequalities for each (y_1^0, y_2^0) designated by the index h:

$$C(y_1^0, y_2^0) - \alpha_{h,k} C(y_1^{0'}, y_2^{0'}) \leqslant b_{h,k} \quad . \quad . \quad . \quad (13.12)$$
over all h, k

[1] Howard's value determination operation uses the inverse matrix $[I-\alpha P]^{-1}$ to compute costs for a given policy, where P is a stochastic matrix associated with the policy and $0 < \alpha < 1$. Here, from (13.11) we see that the inverse matrix $[I-A]^{-1}$ will be used to compute the $C(y_1^0, y_2^0)$ for a given selection of x_i's, where A is a Leontief matrix with one discount factor entered on each row. A special computer code using Howard's approach and taking advantage of the structure of the matrix A is being developed to compute solutions for problems having more than two producing areas.

[2] de Ghellinck (1960) has noted that Howard's method is a specialization of the simplex method of linear programming for this problem which allows changing of an entire basis at each iteration.

The problem now may be stated as the primal linear programming problem:

$$\text{Maximize } \sum_h C(y_1^0, y_2^0) \quad . \quad . \quad . \quad . \quad (13.13)$$

subject to the constraints (13.12)

Since the primal problem has many more constraints than variables, solutions may be computed more easily by applying the simplex method to the dual of (13.13):[1]

$$\text{Minimize } \sum_{h, k} b_{h, k}\, u_{h, k} \quad . \quad . \quad . \quad . \quad (13.14)$$

subject to

$$
\begin{bmatrix}
1 & 1\ldots & & & & & \\
-\alpha_{1,1} & & 1 & 1\ldots & & & \\
& -\alpha_{1,2} & -\alpha_{2,1} & & 1 & 1\ldots & \\
& & & -\alpha_{2,2} & -\alpha_{3,1} & & \\
& & & & -\alpha_{3,2} & & \\
& & & & & & -\alpha_{m,n_m} \\
& & & & -\alpha_{m,n_m-1} & & \\
& & & \ldots 1 & & 1 &
\end{bmatrix}
\begin{bmatrix}
u_{1,1} \\
u_{1,2} \\
\cdot \\
\cdot \\
\cdot \\
\cdot \\
\cdot \\
u_{m,n_m}
\end{bmatrix}
=
\begin{bmatrix}
1 \\
1 \\
\cdot \\
\cdot \\
\cdot \\
\cdot \\
\cdot \\
1
\end{bmatrix}
$$

and $u_{h, k} \geqslant 0$ for all h, k

The values of the $C(y_1^0, y_2^0)$ which solve (13.13) will now be obtained as the dual solution to the dual linear programming problem (13.14).

Some computational results

Solutions for several two producing area problems were computed with the linear programming formulation (13.14). In these problems, each area has the identical plant investment cost function $f_i(x_i D_i) = k(x_i D_i)^a$, and the typical parameters $k = 1 \cdot 0$, $a = 0 \cdot 70$ and $r = 0 \cdot 10$ were used for comparison with the results of Chapter 12. The demand growth rate D_1 in area 1 was fixed at $1 \cdot 0$, and three values of D_2

---

[1] The dual formulation (13.14) has the structure of the general weighted distribution problem (see Dantzig (1963), p. 420).

were considered: $1 \cdot 0$, $0 \cdot 5$ and $0 \cdot 25$. For each combination of demand growth rates, solutions were computed for values of $p_{21} = p_{12} = 0 \cdot 10$, $0 \cdot 25$, $0 \cdot 50$ and $1 \cdot 0$.

The y_i^0 were restricted to integer values, and upper limits on the y_i^0 were chosen arbitrarily based on results computed using the methods of Chapter 2 for the extreme cases $p_{ij} = 0$ and $+ \infty$. For example, the largest problem was obtained for $D_2 = 0 \cdot 25$; in this case the limits $0 \leqslant y_1^0 \leqslant 15$ and $0 \leqslant y_2^0 \leqslant 30$ were used, and plant sizes were restricted to $5 \leqslant x_1 \leqslant 15$ and $5 \leqslant x_2 \leqslant 30$. This gave a linear programming problem with 46 rows and 757 columns which was solved for all four values of p_{ij} in about three minutes on the

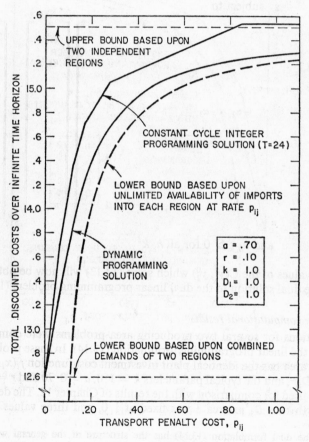

Figure 13.2a.—Two Region Problem—Solution Costs from Initial Position (0, 0)

Stanford University IBM 7090 computer.[1] (There is no evidence that these arbitrary limits affected the solutions.)

The solution costs obtained for policies from the initial position $(y_1^0, y_2^0) = (0, 0)$ are given in Figures 13.2a and 13.2b for two demand

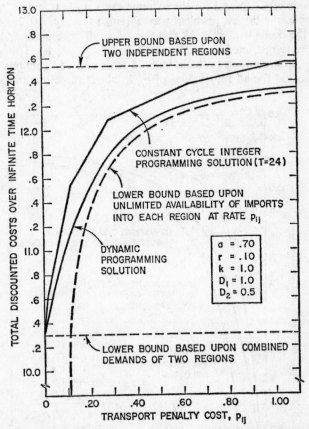

Figure 13.2b.—Two Region Problem—Solution Costs from Initial Position (0, 0)

[1] The solutions were obtained with the M3 Linear and Separable Programming System provided by the Standard Oil Company of California. Such features of the code as multiple objective forms and advanced starts were useful for this problem. Most important was the option of saving several columns at each pass through the matrix to be eligible for entry into the basis before the next complete pass. This option was used to approach the multiple basis change advantage of Howard's algorithm, and frequently 25 to 40% of the basis columns were changed in a single matrix pass.

growth rate combinations. Also given are the costs from the constant cycle integer programming formulation of Chapter 12 and a lower bound on the costs based upon allowing unlimited availability of imports into each area at the penalty rate p_{ij}. Solutions obtained by

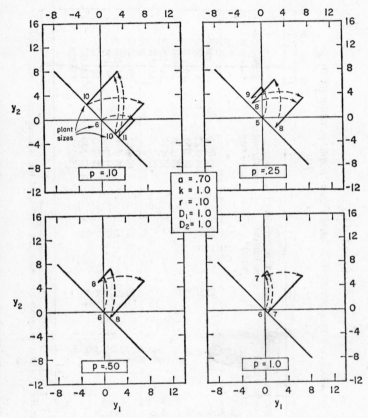

Figure 13.3a.—Dynamic Programming Policies from Initial Position (0, 0)

dynamic and integer programming are also compared in Table 13.1. In all cases the reduction in costs is less than $3 \cdot 5\%$.

Figures 13.3a, 13.3b and 13.3c give the solution policies from starting point (0, 0) for the twelve examples. A strictly constant cycle policy is not found in any case, but all policies converge rapidly to a steady-state constant cycle form in which each area receives shipments from the other at some time. In Figure 13.3a with $D_1 = D_2$

INVESTMENTS FOR CAPACITY EXPANSION

TABLE 13.1

Two producing area problem-solutions from initial position (0, 0)
$(k = 1 \cdot 0, a = 0 \cdot 70, r = 0 \cdot 10)$

Case	p_{ij}	Integer programming cycle length (years)		Dynamic programming cycle length (years)*		Integer programming-total costs	Dynamic programming-total costs	Cost reduction (%)
		x_1	x_2	x_1	x_2			
	0·00	12	12	13	13	12·620	12·598	0·2
	0·10	8	8	10	10	14·122	13·657	3·3
$D_1 = 1 \cdot 0$	0·25	8	8	8	8	14·955	14·581	2·5
$D_2 = 1 \cdot 0$	0·50	6	8	8	8	15·238	15·061	1·2
	1·00	6	6	7	7	15·537	15·286	1·6
	∞	6	6	7	7	15·537	15·510	0·2
	0·00	12	12	10	20	10·402	10·299	1·0
	0·10	12	12	11	11	11·359	11·073	2·5
$D_1 = 1 \cdot 0$	0·25	8	8	8	8	11·962	11·675	2·4
$D_2 = 0 \cdot 5$	0·50	8	8	8	8	12·262	12·115	1·2
	1·00	6	8	7	7	12·530	12·323	1·6
	∞	6	6	7	7	12·551	12·528	0·2

NOTE: * The cycle length for the dynamic programming solution is that of the ultimate steady-state cycle.

$= 1 \cdot 0$ and $p_{ij} = 0 \cdot 25, 0 \cdot 50$ and $1 \cdot 0$, the ultimate cycle has the length of the optimal policy for the single-area model with time-phased imports in Chapter 10. A balance is reached in which each area may make its decisions as though capacity in the other were unlimited at all times.

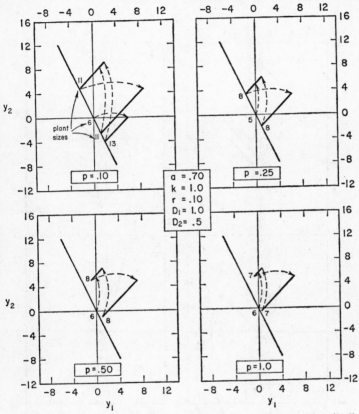

Figure 13.3b.—Dynamic Programming Policies from Initial Position (0, 0)

In most of the examples, the steady-state cycle lengths are the same in both areas. If demands are sufficiently unbalanced and penalty rates sufficiently low, we see in the case of Figure 13.3c with $p_{ij} = 0 \cdot 10$ that the areas may have different cycle lengths: two plants are constructed in area 1 for each in area 2. Note that the area in which the first plant is constructed may shift as the penalty rate changes.

The steady-state cycle lengths obtained by dynamic programming are compared with the integer programming cycle lengths in Table 13.1. The correspondence is very close, especially since the integer programming formulation restricted x_i to the values of 1, 2, 3, 4, 6, 8, 12 and 24. The cycle lengths (and plant sizes) tend to decrease for either method as the penalty rate p_{ij} rises.

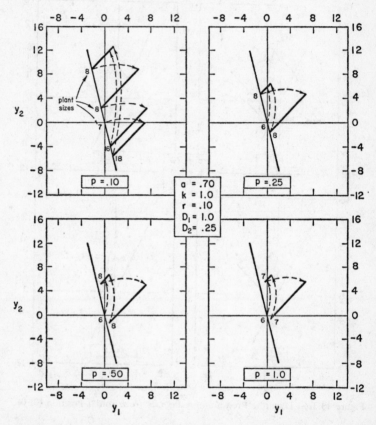

Figure 13.3c.—Dynamic Programming Policies from Initial Position (0, 0)

Figures 13.4a and 13.4b give the complete set of policy solutions from all initial positions for two cases. In Figure 13.4a—regardless of the initial conditions—convergence to a common steady-state cycle is attained after just a few plants have been constructed. In Figure 13.4b, with a higher penalty rate, there is a family of steady-state cycles. Depending upon initial conditions, one or another of these cycles is reached. In both cases (as in all other examples computed) solution policies avoid the origin. I.e. it pays to stagger the construction dates so that both areas do not run out of excess capacity simultaneously.

In Figures 13.4a and 13.4b, during the transient interval before reaching a steady-state cycle there are several cases where the plant

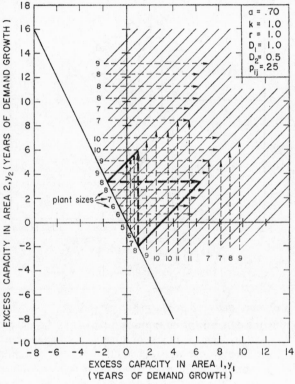

Figure 13.4a.—Dynamic Programming Policies

size selected *increases* as the penalty rate p_{ij} increases from $0 \cdot 25$ to $0 \cdot 50$. One of these cases is the construction decision for excess capacity path $P(10, 0)$. In Figure 13.4a with $p_{ij} = 0 \cdot 25$, the decision is to build a plant capable of supplying 7 years of demand growth. In Figure 13.4b with $p_{ij} = 0 \cdot 50$, a plant is constructed to supply 8 years of demand growth.

P

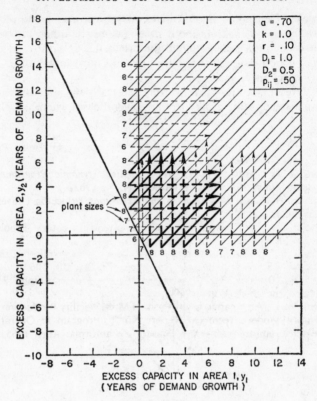

Figure 13.4b.—Dynamic Programming Policies

Problems of more than two producing areas

In principle, the dynamic programming methods of this chapter may be used to solve problems with any number of producing areas. Each additional producing area adds substantially to the computational burden. For example, if we wish to allow m positive values of y_1^0 in each of n areas, the number of excess capacity paths to be considered is approximately $n \cdot (m + \frac{1}{2})^{n-1}$. If we pick $m = 10$, there are roughly 21 paths for $n = 2$, 330 for $n = 3$, and 4,640 for $n = 4$. Given a set of policies, solving for the costs associated with each path for $n = 4$ involves solving a set of 4,640 equations in 4,640 unknowns. Fortunately, this task is greatly simplified since each equation relates only two unknowns. But if an average of 20 decisions from each path must be tested, the total number of decisions approaches 100,000. The data preparation task for these decisions is formidable by itself. It would seem, therefore, that given present computing limitations a problem involving more than four areas is beyond the reach of dynamic programming.

REFERENCES

Bellman, R. E., *Dynamic Programming*, Princeton University Press, Princeton, N. J., 1957.

Bellman, R. E., and S. E. Dreyfus, *Applied Dynamic Programming*, Princeton University Press, Princeton, N. J., 1962.

Dantzig, G. B., *Linear Programming and Extensions*, Princeton University Press, Princeton, N. J., 1963.

d'Epenoux, F., 'A Probabilistic Production and Inventory Problem', *Management Science*, October 1963.

de Ghellinck, G., 'Les Problèmes de Décisions Séquentielles', *Cahiers de Centre d'Étude de Recherche Operationnelle*, Brussels, 1960.

Howard, R., *Dynamic Programming and Markov Processes*, John Wiley and Sons, Inc., New York, 1960.

Zangwill, W. I., 'A Dynamic Multi-Product Multi-Facility Production and Inventory Model', Technical Report No. 1, Program in Operations Research, Stanford University, Stanford, California, April 1965.

CHAPTER 14

INDIAN CASE STUDIES—
CONSTANT CYCLE TIME POLICIES

ALAN S. MANNE[1]

Principal results

In three of the Indian industries studied (caustic soda, cement and nitrogenous fertilizers), it would have been a gross oversimplification to proceed as though the alternative producing areas were indistinguishable from each other, or as though there were negligible costs in transporting the finished product to the consuming markets. It is for these cases (with up to 15 individual producing areas) that the heuristic algorithm SLOT was specifically designed. Chapter 12 has already described the algorithm's principal characteristics: the restriction to constant cycle time policies, the return to a point of regeneration every T periods over an infinite horizon, the arbitrary choice of initial values for the minor cycle lengths x_i and the first onstream dates y_i, and the arbitrary order in which the regions are examined. Even though the procedure is not guaranteed to arrive at an optimal solution, there is considerable evidence that its performance is almost as satisfactory as dynamic programming for the case of two producing areas.

The principal results for the Indian case studies may be summarized as follows:

(1) Table 14.1 compares the best plans found through SLOT with the best single- and two-phase solutions reported in Chapters 5–7. According to these calculations, SLOT would lead to cost reductions ranging from $4 \cdot 6\%$ (cement) to $8 \cdot 4\%$ (caustic soda), and to $14 \cdot 1\%$ (nitrogenous fertilizers). These reductions appear substantial—even after making allowances for the margins of error in each numerical parameter entering the calculations.

(2) Cost reductions are achieved primarily through more complex time-phasing patterns than can be managed through hand calculations. E.g. the pattern recommended for caustic soda is that a plant be built every 6 years in Maharashtra, every 12 years in Madhya Pradesh, and every 24 years in all other producing areas. With demands growing over time, the overall investment programme can

---

[1] The author is indebted to Donald Erlenkotter for helpful comments and for assistance with the numerical analysis.

be planned so that a large, low-cost unit will eventually be constructed in the vicinity of each market having an adequate supply of raw materials.

TABLE 14.1

Cost comparison between best plans

	Discounted costs (Rs. millions)		% reduction
	Best single- and two-phase solutions reported in chapters 5–7	Best plans found through SLOT	
Caustic soda	1,204*	1,103	8·4%
Cement	7,773†	7,414	4·6
Nitrogenous fertilizers	6,096‡	5,236	14·1

NOTES: * *Source:* Table 5.7; two-phase five-year cycles, regional market areas; West alternates with three other regions.

† *Source:* Table 6.8; two-phase cycles; coal transport at conventional rates for coal.

‡ *Source:* Table 7.8, case B; single-phase, regional centre perpetually supplies all states in its region.

(3) Because of reluctance to extrapolate cost curves into unknown territory, we have ruled out the possibility of constructing units larger than those existing anywhere else in the world at the beginning of the Fourth Plan. Both in the hand computations and in SLOT, this maximum size limit is typically an effective constraint, and so there is little difference between the plant sizes recommended by the two procedures. Under other circumstances (e.g. in a country with a far smaller internal market than India), this coincidence in plant size recommendations is unlikely.

A typical time-phasing pattern

Table 14.2 contains a typical time-phasing pattern for the nitrogenous fertilizer industry. Recall that the admissible construction sequences for each producing region i are defined in terms of two decision variables: x_i (the minor cycle length) and y_i (the first on-stream date). An arbitrary initial value is assigned to each decision variable; local optimizations are performed in an arbitrary order of the producing regions; and the procedure is terminated when no further reduction in costs is obtainable through changing the x_i and y_i values in a *single* region.

TABLE 14.2

A typical time-phasing pattern for the nitrogenous fertilizer industry

Producing regions listed in order of local optimization (random ordering number 1)	x_i (minor cycle length)		y_i (first onstream date)	
	Initial value*	Terminal value†	Initial value	Terminal value†
3. Orissa	24	24	0	23
4. West Bengal	12	12	0	10
5. Punjab, Jammu & Kashmir	8	8	0	5
7. Uttar Pradesh, East	8	8	0	3
10. Madhya Pradesh	12	12	0	9
12. Andhra Pradesh	12	12	0	8
14. Mysore	12	12	0	5
6. Rajasthan	12	12	0	4
15. Madras	12	12	0	5
9. Gujarat	12	12	0	3
2. Bihar	12	12	0	2
8. Uttar Pradesh, West	12	12	0	1
1. Assam	24	24	0	10
11. Maharashtra	6	6	0	0
13. Kerala	24	24	0	0

NOTES: * Initial values of x_i were assigned the maximum value consistent with a plant size limit of 250 thousand tons/year of ammonia. E.g. in Maharashtra (region 11) the annual demand increment $D_{11} = 37 \cdot 3$ thousand tons. With plant sizes limited to a maximum of 250 thousand tons, this demand increment is compatible with $x_{11} = 1, 2, 3, 4$ or 6 years, but not with $x_{11} = 8, 12$ or 24 years.

† In moving from the initial to the terminal values of x_i and y_i, costs changed as follows:

	Discounted costs (Rs. millions)	
	initial value	terminal value
Manufacturing costs subject to economies-of-scale	6,779	4,447
Transport costs (including naphtha)	570	789
Total costs	7,349	5,236

Listed in Table 14.2 are both the initial and the terminal value of x_i and y_i. In each computing run for the nitrogenous fertilizer industry, the identical initial values were employed. The first on-stream date y_i was placed at zero in all producing regions, and the cycle time variables x_i were each assigned the maximum value consistent with a plant size limit of 250 thousand tons/year. These initial values constitute a logical extreme—minimizing the cost of shipping products to the consuming locations and also maximizing the initial quantity of idle capacity.

In order to improve upon the initially specified values for each decision variable, the heuristic routine SLOT examines the producing regions in an arbitrarily specified sequence, and—whenever a cost reduction is obtainable—resets the decision variables accordingly. E.g. Table 14.2 indicates that the regions were examined according to random ordering number 1—first adjusting the decision variables for region 3, then those for regions 4, 5, 7, . . . 11, 13—then again regions 3, 4, 5, 7, . . . 11, 13 until no further cost reduction is obtainable through changing the cycle lengths and first onstream dates in a single producing region.

In Table 14.2, the terminal values of the x_i are identical with their initial values. Since the initial values were chosen so that the resulting plant sizes x_iD_i would be roughly equal to the largest existing anywhere in the world at the beginning of the Fourth Plan, this means that the upper bound on plant size turned out to be an effective constraint. With but a few exceptions, similar results were obtained in all calculations for each of the three Indian industries studied.

Although the arbitrarily specified sequence for local optimization has virtually no effect upon the cycle lengths x_i, this ordering exerts a significant effect upon the terminal values of the onstream dates y_i. (Again see Table 14.2.) The earlier a region is examined, the longer delayed tends to be its first plant. (Most exceptions to this generalization are to be explained by the constraint that $y_i < x_i$.)

Order of local optimization—some experiments

Since the recommended time-phasing patterns are heavily influenced by an arbitrary computational detail (the order of local optimization), we conducted a number of experiments, and have summarized the results in Table 14.3. For each industry, five randomly chosen sequences were employed—also one sequence in which the regions were examined in ascending order of their demand increments D_i and another sequence in descending order of D_i.

Even though the order of examination has a substantial effect upon the detailed time-phasing of new plants, it does not appear to have a profound effect upon the level of total costs. E.g. among the seven orderings for the nitrogenous fertilizer industry the two lowest cost figures are Rs. 5,236 and Rs. 5,268 millions, a difference of 0·6%.

Conceivably a much larger sample of orderings would lead to a much lower value of costs, but one suspects that there are sharply diminishing returns to such sampling investigations.[1]

TABLE 14.3

Experiments with order of local optimization

	Manufacturing costs subject to economies-of-scale	Transport costs*	Total costs
Caustic soda			
Random ordering number 1	1,018	104	1,122
,, ,, ,, 2	1,018	94	1,112
,, ,, ,, 3	1,017	108	1,125
,, ,, ,, 4	1,005	98	1,103
,, ,, ,, 5	1,032	98	1,130
Ascending order of D_i	1,027	119	1,146
Descending order of D_i	1,067	117	1,184
Cement			
Random ordering number 1	4,566	2,860	7,426
,, ,, ,, 2	4,573	2,859	7,432
,, ,, ,, 3	4,599	2,833	7,432
,, ,, ,, 4	4,554	2,860	7,414
,, ,, ,, 5	4,620	2,850	7,470
Ascending order of D_i	4,591	2,871	7,462
Descending order of D_i	4,608	2,822	7,430
Nitrogenous fertilizers			
Random ordering number 1	4,447	789	5,236
,, ,, ,, 2	4,497	775	5,272
,, ,, ,, 3	4,437	874	5,311
,, ,, ,, 4	4,432	836	5,268
,, ,, ,, 5	4,565	818	5,383
Ascending order of D_i	4,277	994	5,271
Descending order of D_i	4,581	770	5,351

NOTE: * Includes cost of transporting raw materials: coal for cement and naphtha for nitrogenous fertilizers.

From the policy-maker's viewpoint, it is important to know that costs are so insensitive to order of examination—hence insensitive to the detailed time-phasing of new plants. Example: There is little difference between the overall costs for random orderings number 1 and number 4 in the nitrogenous fertilizer industry, and yet there are significant political differences for Orissa. Although both plans call for building a large unit every 24 years in that state, the first one

[1] In order to perform the calculations for one specific ordering of the producing regions, our computational routine absorbed from three to ten minutes on the Stanford University I.B.M. 7090 machine. With sampling costs of this magnitude, we were reluctant to take more than seven samples for each of the three industries.

would delay that plant for 23 years, and the other would delay it for only 5 years. The pressure bloc from Orissa would not be indifferent to these two alternatives!

Time paths of excess capacity

In the cement, caustic soda, and nitrogenous fertilizer industries, our calculations were based upon the restriction that India's production capacity be capable of satisfying the domestic demand at all times.[1] As a result of this self-sufficiency restriction, it is clear that each new plant will lead to excess capacity somewhere within the economy, and that this excess will persist until it is absorbed by the growth in demand.

For any one industry, the time path of excess capacity will depend both upon the aggregate rate of growth of demand and also upon the specific choice of plant size, location and time-phasing. Illustrative examples are given in Tables 14.4–14.6. (These tables are based upon setting the decision variables at levels that correspond to the lowest cost solution found in the numerical experiments with each industry.) Excess capacities are shown year-by-year from time 0 through 24. Note that the capacity increments are all scheduled in such a way that the excess in each producing region drops to zero (a point of regeneration) at time 24, and every 24 years thereafter.

For the two-region model discussed in Chapters 4, 12 and 13, it has already been shown that the optimal amount of excess capacity depends upon balancing the transport penalties against the benefits that accrue from delaying the investment in new capacity. Our 'two-phase cycles' were really based upon the following rule-of-thumb: If it pays to defer the construction of a new plant and to incur transport penalties meanwhile, then it pays to defer that new plant as long as possible without violating the overall self-sufficiency constraint. According to Tables 14.4–14.6, this heuristic rule works well. The costs and benefits are such that it is desirable to reduce the entire country's excess capacity to near-zero levels before bringing new units onstream. Even in the cement industry with its relatively high transport penalty costs, it generally pays to let the excess capacity drop below 600 thousands tons (roughly the size of a single new unit) before constructing another new unit. With further insights of this type—as well as with analytical results through dynamic programming—it is safe to predict that SLOT will be rapidly superseded by still more powerful computing techniques for preinvestment programming.

[1] Throughout this volume, the assumption of self-sufficiency has been relaxed only in the case of the aluminium industry, chapter 3.

TABLE 14.4

Time path for caustic soda industry, lowest cost solution found through SLOT
(random ordering number 4; discounted costs = Rs. 1,103 millions)

Year t	Capacity increment (thousands of tons) in region i at year t															Cumulative capacity available immediately prior to year t (thousands of tons)	Cumulative demand at year t (thousands of tons)	Excess capacity available immediately prior to year t (thousands of tons)
	1. Assam	2. Bihar	3. Orissa	4. West Bengal	5. Punjab, J. & K.	6. Rajasthan	7. Uttar Pradesh, East	8. Uttar Pradesh, West	9. Gujarat	10. Madhya Pradesh	11. Maharashtra	12. Andhra Pradesh	13. Kerala	14. Mysore	15. Madras			
0											101·4					0·0	0·0	0·0
1													88·8			101·4	58·6	42·8
2																190·2	117·2	73·0
3							81·6									190·2	175·8	14·4
4										100·8						271·8	234·4	37·4
5																372·6	293·0	79·6
6											101·4					372·6	351·6	21·0
7																474·0	410·2	63·8
8								62·4								474·0	468·8	5·2
9														81·6		536·4	527·4	9·0
10		48·0														618·0	586·0	32·0
11			26·4			31·2										666·0	644·6	21·4
12											101·4					723·6	703·2	20·4
13																825·0	761·8	63·2
14				115·2												825·0	820·4	4·6
15																940·2	879·0	61·2
16										100·8						940·2	937·6	2·6
17															81·6	1,041·0	996·2	44·8
18											101·4					1,122·6	1,054·8	67·8
19																1,224·0	1,113·4	110·6
20	45·6															1,224·0	1,172·0	52·0
21												26·4				1,269·6	1,230·6	39·0
22									67·2							1,296·0	1,289·2	6·8
23					43·2											1,363·2	1,347·8	15·4
24											101·4					1,406·4	1,406·4	0·0

Time path for cement industry, lowest cost solution found through SLO1 (random ordering number 4; discounted costs = Rs. 7,414 millions*)

Year t	Capacity increment† (thousands of tons) in region i at year t										Cumulative capacity available immediately prior to year t (thousands of tons)	Cumulative demand at year t (thousands of tons)	Excess capacity available immediately prior to year t (thousands of tons)
	1. Assam	2. Bihar	3. Orissa	5. Punjab, J. & K.	6. Rajasthan	9. Gujarat	10. Madhya Pradesh	12. Andhra Pradesh	14. Mysore	15. Madras			
0		638				558	592				0	0	0
1				672				756	724		1,788	1,734	54
2		638			645	558	592				3,940	3,468	472
3			712								6,373	5,202	1,171
4		638				558	592				7,085	6,936	149
5	504				645				724		8,873	8,670	203
6		638				558	592				10,746	10,404	342
7								756		656	12,534	12,138	396
8		638			645	558	592				13,946	13,872	74
9				672					724		16,379	15,606	773
10		638				558	592				17,775	17,340	435
11			712		645						19,563	19,074	489
12		638				558	592				20,920	20,808	112
13	504							756	724		22,708	22,542	166
14		638			645	558	592				24,692	24,276	416
15										656	27,125	26,010	1,115
16		638				558	592				27,781	27,744	37
17				672	645				724		29,569	29,478	91
18		638				558	592				31,610	31,212	398
19			712					756			33,398	32,946	452
20		638			645	558	592				34,866	34,680	186
21	504								724		37,299	36,414	885
22		638				558	592				38,527	38,148	379
23					645					656	40,315	39,882	433
24		638				558	592				41,616	41,616	0

NOTES: * Costs calculated on basis of alternation between a 'new unit' and a 'substantial expansion' in each producing region.
† Because of lack of limestone, no production capacity is shown for the five following consuming regions: 4. West Bengal; 7. Uttar Pradesh East; 8. Uttar Pradesh, West; 11. Maharashtra; 13. Kerala.

TABLE 14.6

Time path for nitrogenous fertilizer industry, lowest cost solution found through SLOT (random ordering number 1; discounted costs = Rs. 5,236 millions)

Year t	\multicolumn{15}{c}{Capacity increment (thousands of tons) i at year t}															Cumulative capacity available immediately prior to year t (thousands of tons)	Cumulative demand at year t (thousands of tons)	Excess capacity available immediately prior to year t (thousands of tons)
	1. Assam	2. Bihar	3. Orissa	4. West Bengal	5. Punjab, J. & K.	6. Rajasthan	7. Uttar Pradesh, East	8. Uttar Pradesh, West	9. Gujarat	10. Madhya Pradesh	11. Maharashtra	12. Andhra Pradesh	13. Kerala	14. Mysore	15. Madras			
0																0·00	0·00	0·00
1											223·80		206·64			430·44	260·89	169·55
2								226·92								657·36	521·78	135·58
3		223·56														880·92	782·67	98·25
4							226·96		180·60							1,288·48	1,043·56	244·92
5						172·80										1,461·28	1,304·45	156·83
6					208·24									132·84	237·36	2,039·72	1,565·34	474·38
7											223·80					2,263·52	1,826·23	437·29
8																2,263·52	2,087·12	176·40
9												223·80				2,487·32	2,348·01	139·31
10										134·28						2,621·60	2,608·90	12·70
11	161·52			203·52												2,986·64	2,869·79	116·85
12							226·96									3,213·60	3,130·68	82·92
13											223·80					3,437·40	3,391·57	45·83
14					208·24			226·92								3,872·56	3,652·46	220·10
15		223·56														4,096·12	3,913·35	182·77
16									180·60							4,276·72	4,174·24	102·48
17						172·80										4,449·52	4,435·13	14·39
18														132·84	237·36	4,819·72	4,696·02	123·70
19											223·80					5,043·52	4,956·91	86·61
20							226·96									5,270·48	5,217·80	52·68
21												223·80				5,494·28	5,478·69	15·59
22					208·24					134·28						5,836·80	5,739·58	97·22
23				203·52												6,040·32	6,000·47	39·85
24			221·04													6,261·36	6,261·36	0·00

NAME INDEX

Aggarwal, B. K., 118
Abramowitz, M., 26

Balassa, B., 146, 148
Banerjee, B. K., 118
Baumol, W. J., 206, 209
Bellman, R., 21, 26, 170, 177, 186, 190, 212, 227
Bergendahl, G., 60
Bierwert, D. V., 20, 26
Birman, I., 20
Buzby, B. R., 20

Chakravarty, S., 24, 26
Charnes, A., 179, 190
Chatterjee, P., 99, 116
Chaudhuri, M. Datta, 32, 48
Chenery, H. B., 25, 26, 31, 47
Chilton, C. H., 37, 47
Coleman, J. R., Jr., 32, 47
Committee on Transport Policy and Coordination, 92, 94
Cooper, L., 60, 71
Cooper, W. W., 179, 190

Dadachanji, C. J., 143, 148
Dantzig, G. B., 218, 227
Dreyfus, S., 21, 26, 170, 177, 186, 190, 212, 227

Economic Commission for Latin America, 20, 27, 77, 94, 140
d'Epenoux, F., 217, 227
Erlenkotter, D., 44, 49, 193, 201, 228

Fertiliser Association of India, 119, 122, 139

de Ghellinck, G., 217, 227
Ghosh, A., 112, 116
Gilmore, P. C., 196, 209
Gomory, R. E., 196, 209
Grant, E. L., 40, 47

Hadley, G., 167, 177, 178, 190
Hahn, R. F., 33, 47
Hamburger, M. J., 60, 71
Harberger, A. C., 33, 47
Healey, J. M., 93, 94, 109, 117
Holt, C. C., 23, 26
Howard, R., 217, 227
Hufschmidt, M. M., 33, 48

Indian Railway Conference Association, 132
Indian Statistical Institute, 110, 117, 123, 139
Institut Français du Pétrole, 30, 45, 48
Ireson, W. G., 40, 47

Joint Technical Group on Transport Planning, 108, 117

Karlin, S., 36, 48
Khatau, R. M., 95, 117
Krone, F. A., 20, 26
Krutilla, J., 48
Kuehn, A. A., 60, 71
Kuhn, H. W., 206, 209
Kumar, L., 42

Lefeber, L., 24, 26, 32, 48
Loginov, Z. I., 20

McDowell, I., 32, 48
Malinvaud, E., 25, 26
Manne, A. S., 23, 24, 26, 32, 48, 60, 71, 157, 161, 177, 185, 190, 206, 209
Marglin, S. A., 33, 48
Margolis, J., 48
Markowitz, H. M., 71
Massé, P., 33, 48
Matthews, R. C. O., 33, 47
Minc, L. E., 20
Modigliani, F., 23, 26
Mukherjee, 125, 140
Muth, J. F., 23, 26

SUBJECT INDEX